THE WORLD'S FINEST

THE WORLD'S FINEST
JAMAICA BLUE MOUNTAIN® COFFEE

Norma Benghiat

Ian Randle Publishers
Kingston   Miami

First published in Jamaica, 2008 by
Ian Randle Publishers
11 Cunningham Avenue
Box 686
Kingston 6
www.ianrandlepublishers.com

National Library of Jamaica Cataloguing in Publication Data

Benghiat, Norma
      The world's finest : Jamaica Blue Mountain® coffee / Norma
Benghiat
        p. : ill. ; cm.

     Include index

     ISBN 978-976-637-114-2 (hardback)

     1. Coffee – Jamaica 2. Coffee industry - Jamaica
     I. Title

     633.73   dc 21

Cover Photograph by Toni-Ann McKenzie
Cover and book design by Ian Randle Publishers
Printed in China

Illustration Credits

Ray Chen p. 26-27, 53, 60-61, 68-69, 80-81, 86, 87, 89, 93, 97, 105, 107,
108-109, 110, 115, 128-129
Franz Marzouca p. 122-123, 148, 151, 152, 154, 158, 164, 172, 176, 182-
183, 184, 188, 191, 200
Toni-Ann McKenzie p. 1, 49, 54, 59, 73, 75, 76, 98, 100-101, 104, 113,
117, 134-144, 171

The images on p. 31, 33, 35, 37, 39, 41, 43, 45 and 47, are reproduced with
the permission of the Coffee Industry Board of Jamaica and the kind
assistance of Coffee Industries Limited.

The image on p. 6 Coaling a Steamer at Kingston Jamaica. London: The
Illustrated London News, 1888 courtesy of the Historical Museum of
Southern Florida.

Copyright in the images on the following pages has expired:
p. 2 Coffee Arabica; p. 3 Carte d'Amerique 1774 Guillaume Delisle; p. 5
The Island of Jamaica 1720 Herman Moll; p.8-9 Einer Sultanin wird eine
Tasse Kaffee von einer Sklavin überreicht 1747 Charles André van Loo;
p. 13 An Arab Trader's Party. From Stanley and the White Heroes in
Africa (etc.) (H.B. Scammel, 1890); p. 15 Meddah-story teller; p. 18-19 A
Coffee house in Palestine; p. 20 Zimmermann's Coffeehaus, Leipzig
Engraving by Georg Schreiber, 18th century; p. 23 Discussing the War in
a Paris Café Frederick Barnard Illustrated London News 1870; p. 25 New
Amsterdam, recently called New York (Nieuw Jorck), and now retaken by
the Netherlands 24 Aug 1673 Hugo Allard; p. 28 Gabriel deClieu; p. 144
Moka coffee machine Alexandre Albore.

Tia Maria® liqueur bottle photo ©2007 Malibu Kahlua International,
White Plains, N.Y.

The Tia Maria name, label and logo are registered trademarks of Tia
Maria Ltd and used under permission. All rights reserved.

Every effort has been made to trace the copyright holders of photographs
and illustrations used in this book, and we apologise for any unintentional
omissions or errors. We would be pleased to insert the appropriate
acknowledgments or amendments in all subsequent editions of this
book.

The publisher would like to thank Strawberry Hill, The Coffee Mill and
Café Blue for their assistance with this project.

Contents

To my family

Acknowledgements

I wish to thank the many people who have given of their time and knowledge for the writing of this book, and in particular Keble Munn and David Evans for giving me both personal and professional details of their involvement in the coffee industry and Alex and Dorothy Twyman of "The Tavern" for allowing photographs to be taken at their property and Eleanor Jones for information on Cold Spring estate.

I also wish to thank the Coffee Industry Board, in particular Loreen Walker, Hervin Willis, Dave Gordon and Mr. Waugh for their help and for permission to use the words, Jamaica Blue Mountain® Coffee, the Moy Hall Coffee Factory for photographing the processing of coffee, the National Library of Jamaica, for research material, the University of the West Indies Library, particularly for allowing me to quote from the Stowe papers: Middleton and Merryman's Field Coffee Plantations and Letters; the Ministry of Agriculture and Lands for permission to quote from *A Short Economic History with Special Reference to Jamaica* by D.W. Rodriquez, Brett Ashmeade Hawkins for the photograph of the Middleton overseer's house and coffee works, and Estate Industries and Malibu Kahlua International for the use of the Tia Maria® recipes.

I would also like to thank the following for the use of photographs of coffee houses, namely, Whitfield Hall — Mr. and Mrs. John Allgrove; Abby Green — Mr. and Mrs. Keble Munn; Sherwood Forrest — RSW Estates Limited; Arntully — Mr. Lloyd Dixon; Bellevue — The University of the West Indies and Craighton House, Jamaica UCC Blue Mountain Coffee Company Limited.

I would also like to thank the ceramists, Margaret McGhie and Phillip Supersad for the loan of several pieces of their artwork; Azan's in The Springs, for tableware; Susie's Bakery and Coffee Bar for some of the desserts and Claude Hamilton for orchids from Hamlyn Orchids. Thanks also to Pauline Simmonds, Elrys Kensington and Blondine DuQuesnay, my sister, and Ray Chen, the photographer who bravely made the trips with me to some of the coffee houses high in the rugged Blue Mountains.

Introduction

Coffea arabica L.

As a child growing up on the plains of St. Catherine, the only time that I saw green (unroasted) coffee was when my mother brought it home from the market. I never saw a coffee plant until I was nine years old, when I visited family friends in the hills of Guanaboa Vale, near Spanish Town. For coffee, unlike sugar cane, was grown in the cool mountainous areas of the island, sometimes almost inaccessible, and where the roads were not the best.

A chance meeting with Professor David Buisseret, at Middleton, in 1978, turned out to be significant. He told my husband and me that our piece of land on the Hope River, comprising three old coffee barbecues, had been the mill area for the Middleton coffee plantation, which at one time had belonged to the Dukes of Buckingham and Chandos. The house across and above the bridle path was the original Great House. This chance meeting was to lead to the writing of this book.

"The Jamaican coffee stor

From Abyssinia to the New World

Imagine the present day journey of the *Coffea arabica* plant from its native Abyssinia (Ethiopia) to Arabia, where it was adopted as a religious drink by the Moslems. Its availability and use at Mecca ensured its popularity throughout the Moslem world.

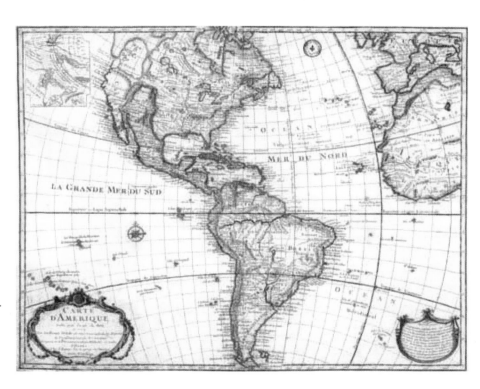

Although no live bean or plant was allowed out of Arabia, human ingenuity found ways and means to enable its escape. Coffee began to be grown in India and other lands, especially the Dutch-held lands of the East that were to supply the early European demand.

Coffee was introduced to Europe in the seventeenth century. Coffee houses became fashionable meeting places where every subject could be discussed. By the time coffee was introduced into

egan in 1978..."

3

the New World, through Martinique, in 1717, the coffee houses in England (though not in other European countries) were already in decline.

From the arabica seeds and plants of Martinique, the coffee plantations of the New World were established. Coffee production in the Caribbean islands was at its peak during the late eighteenth century. At the time of the 1789 revolution in Haiti, that island was the largest coffee producer in the world, annually exporting some 70 million pounds of coffee. But the vast lands and scale of coffee production in Brazil—where slavery lingered much longer than in the Caribbean—would contribute to the decline in production in the islands.

The Jamaican Coffee Story

The Jamaican coffee story began in 1728, when Governor Sir Nicholas Lawes introduced arabica seeds and plants to the island, planting them on his estate at Temple Hall, in the interior hills of St Andrew. The subsequent support of the coffee industry by the House of Assembly was seen not only as an economic measure—because the hilly lands which make up nearly two-thirds of the island were unsuitable for sugar cane cultivation—but also as a means of opening up the interior mountain lands and increasing the island's security. At that time, in fact, coffee production was not a particularly attractive economic venture, as the duty on coffee entering England was kept high in order to encourage tea drinking.

When the duty was finally reduced in the 1790s, a boom period followed, during which Jamaica became one of the world's largest exporters. In 1814, the island produced 34 million pounds of beans for export—though that level of production was never achieved again.

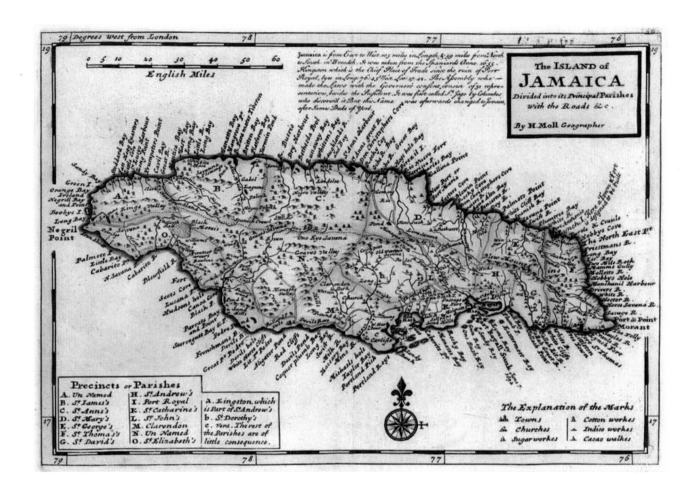

Although records were not kept specifically for the production of what today we call Jamaica Blue Mountain® coffee, it is known that, until 1790, most of Jamaica's coffee was grown in what is now defined as the Blue Mountain coffee area. What was not understood then—and is not fully understood even today—was why the coffee grown in the eastern Blue Mountains developed a superior flavour, unmatched by any coffee grown elsewhere in the world.

The Continental System, which kept British products out of Europe from 1806 to 1814, and Britain's war with America (1812–14) ruined many coffee planters, who had expanded their production only to find nowhere to sell it. The final blow descended in 1838, the year that slavery fully ended in the British Caribbean. Many plantations were cut up into plots and sold or leased to peasant farmers or abandoned. The peasant farmers became the backbone of coffee production. But over the years the quality of the coffee had deteriorated, and in 1948 the Coffee Industry Board was established not only to establish quality guidelines for cultivation and processing but also to buy, process, grade and export all coffee in the island.

In 1983, to increase coffee production, the government deregulated the industry, allowing farmers producing at least 10,000 boxes of cherry coffee to export their own product. Today the coffee industry is expanding chiefly in the defined Blue Mountains growing area. The Japanese government and Japanese coffee importers have invested generously in the best Blue Mountains plantations and are heavily involved in the growing of Blue Mountain coffee on the island. The fact that so much of the product is exported to Japan has driven up the price in Europe and North America, and Jamaica Blue Mountain® coffee is now perceived as a good investment by Jamaicans with money to invest. In a way, coffee has come full circle in Jamaica.

The Early History of Coffee

Although other species of coffee, such as robusta (*Coffea canephora*) and liberica (*C.liberica*), were later found growing wild in other parts of Africa, it was the arabica coffee found in Abyssinia that was responsible for coffee's rise to fame throughout the world. Its origin is steeped in fairytale and legend. It grew wild in the hilly area of Kaffa, one of the districts of Shoa in the southwest of Abyssinia. The nomadic tribes of this area would gather the beans, crush them, add fat and form the mixture into balls, which they carried with them on their long journeys. When chewed, these coffee balls helped to sustain the wanderers and keep them alert for long periods.

The plant seems to have been brought to Arabia around AD 525, when Persia invaded Abyssinia, and to have first been planted in Yemen at elevations of 3,500 (1,067 m) to 6,500 (1982 m) feet above sea level.

"...1880, coffee ha

It is hard to disentangle fact from fiction when exploring the early history of coffee's use by the Arabians. It is said that one day a shepherd named Kaldi noticed that his goats, on their return from grazing in the hills, were excessively frisky, prancing and cavorting in an unusual manner. Curious, the next day he decided to follow them to their grazing grounds in the hills. There he saw them nibbling the leaves and berries of a bush, and after a while they became quite frisky. He plucked some of the berries and chewed them, and in his turn he became more alert and happy and began to dance and roll on the ground.

By chance, a monk from a nearby monastery happened to pass by and noted how high-spirited were the goats and the shepherd. When he remarked on this behaviour to Kaldi, Kaldi showed him the bush. The monk gathered some of the berries and ate them, and they had the same effect on him. He told the other monks of his discovery, and they also tried them, and for the first time they were able to stay alert during the long periods of prayers.

Another popular story is told of Ali-bin Omar al Shadhilo, who became the patron saint of Arab coffee growers and drinkers. Al Shadihilo was charged with misconduct with the king's daughter, who was staying with him for a cure. He was banished with his servants into the mountains of Yusab in the Yemen. There they subsisted on what they could find, including coffee berries, from which they brewed a hot drink. It so happened that the inhabitants of a nearby village were plagued with an itching disease and were cured by drinking the coffee brew concocted by al Shadihilo. He was subsequently pardoned and was able to return home, a hero.

ecome the number one export"

The migration of the plants and beans

Very little information is available for the 1,700 years between AD 525 and the thirteenth century, when it was discovered that a fragrant and appetizing drink could be made by roasting the coffee and adding boiling water to it. This new drink quickly became popular in the holy cities of the East, especially with the dervishes, who viewed it as a divine intervention, as the prophet Mohammed had decreed that wine, which had been the religious drink, was no longer permissible, and the local water was brackish and unpalatable. The dervishes introduced coffee in Mecca and Medina, and in no time pilgrims from all over the Muslim world began to drink it. Coffee shops sprang up everywhere in these cities. The faithful, returning to their respective countries, carried coffee with them and introduced its use to their countrymen.

The sale of coffee beans became a profitable trade for the Arabs, and strict measures were taken to ensure that no fertile beans or plants were taken out of the Arab lands. But as with most protectionist measures, they were of no avail. It is said that in 1505 coffee was taken to Ceylon (now Sri Lanka) by an Arab trader, and about 1600 it was taken from Ceylon to Mysore, India. Another story is that in 1660 an Indian pilgrim, Baba Budan, managed to smuggle seven seeds out of Arabia and planted them on his land at Chikamalgur, in southern India.

Some sources say the plant arrived in Java from India by 1690; for instance, Herman Boerhaave, in his index of the Leyden Gardens, says:

Nicholas Witsen, burgomaster of Amsterdam and Governor of the East India Company, by his letters often advised and desired Van Hoorn, Governor of Batavia to procure from Mocha, in Arabia Felix some berries of the coffee tree, to be sown at Batavia which he having accordingly done, and by the means, about the year 1690, raised many plants from seeds, he sent one over to the Governor of Witsen, who immediately presented it to the garden at Amsterdam of which he as the founder and supporter; it there bore fruit, which in a short time produced many young plants from the seed. (quoted in Ellis 1774, 217)

Other sources say the plant was introduced to Java from India in 1696 by Nicholas Witsen, but that two years later the crop was destroyed by flood and earthquake. Supposedly coffee was subsequently reintroduced in 1699 and successfully established on the Kedawoeng estate, near Batavia. In 1706 plants and berries were sent to the Amsterdam botanical gardens, where they were reared and distributed to other gardens and conservatories in Europe.

The Dutch established coffee plantations in Surinam about 1718. Boerhaave (1720) said that 'In 1714 in order to pay particular compliment to Louis XIV of France presented it to him, sent well packaged to go by sea in a glass contraption 5 ft high'. The plant was in full foliage, having both green and ripe berries. It was seen by the members of the Academy of Science and sent to the Royal Gardens at Marly, where it came under the care of M de Jussieu, the king's professor of botany, who had the year before, written a Memoir, printed in the History of the Academy of Sciences of Paris, in 1713, describing the character of this gem, together with an elegant figure of it taken from a smaller plant, which he had received that year from M. Pancras, burgomaster of Amsterdam and director of the Botanical garden there. (Quoted in Ellis 1774)

The king, the Duke of Orleans and the French Academy all took special interest in the plant, with the intent of establishing it in the colonies. Three attempts were made, the first two unsuccessful. The third was entrusted to Gabriel de Clieu, born in 1686 in Anglequeville sur Saane in Normandy, who had joined the French Navy in 1705 and was promoted to captain in 1720. De Clieu sailed from Nantes in the summer of 1717 (other sources say that the plant arrived in Martinique in 1720 or 1723), but as a result of storms and a shortage of water on board the vessel, only one plant survived. He planted it on his estate, Precheur, on the island of Martinique, and it grew very well, producing many berries, which were first harvested in 1721. It was from this plant that all the coffee plantations of the Caribbean and Central and South America were established.

M. de Clieu became governor of Guadeloupe in 1737, and in 1746 he was presented to Louis XV as 'a distinguished officer to whom the colonies, as well as France itself, and commerce, generally are indebted for the cultivation of coffee'. He died on 30 November 1774 in Paris.

The Dutch established plantations in Surinam in 1718, and some sources say that Cayenne's plantations were established in 1722 when the governor of Cayenne (French Guiana), M. de la Motte Aigron, managed by trickery to bring back a plant from Surinam. It is more likely, however, that the plant was introduced from Martinique.

By the late 1720s, both Surinam and Cayenne were producing appreciable amounts of coffee and were competing commercially against each other. The export of fertile coffee beans from either colony was forbidden—but we shall see how easy it was to smuggle the beans out of the country. In any case, the prohibition seems to have been pointless, since by the 1720s plants and beans from de Clieu's plantations were being exported to other Caribbean countries.

In one way or another, coffee came to Brazil, the country that was to become the world's largest producer of it. In 1727, according to one variation of the story, Surinam and Cayenne became involved in a border dispute. They requested Brazil to arbitrate. A lieutenant colonel in the army, Francisco de Melo Palheta, was despatched with orders from the governor general of Maranhao not only to promptly settle the crisis but to bring back the coffee plant.

At Cayenne, he was welcomed by the governor and his wife. Palheta's surveys and border inspections took a long time, interrupted as they were by visits with the governor's wife. When the surveys were finally complete and the dispute settled, a great banquet was held in Palheta's honour to celebrate the successful mission. The first lady presented him with a bouquet of flowers in which were hidden some coffee plants and seeds.

On his return to Brazil, Palheta resigned his commission in the army and moved to his farm near Para, on the banks of one of the tributaries of the Amazon, where he planted his share of the beans. Within five years, coffee cultivation had spread to Maranhao and Bahia, aided also by monks who grew coffee in the grounds around the monasteries. By 1818 Brazil was selling

75,000 pounds of coffee a year. Five years later the crop was much larger, and the beans began to be noticed on the European market. The single plant nurtured by de Clieu, through its seeds, was the source of all the coffee plantations in the Caribbean and Central America.

Coffee production spread to the Greater Antilles, St. Domingue (Haiti), Puerto Rico, Cuba and Jamaica, where it was introduced by the then governor of the island, Sir Nicholas Lawes, in 1728. The Caribbean islands produced millions of pounds of coffee during the eighteenth and early nineteenth centuries, but thereafter production declined rapidly, as a result of competition from Brazil and Colombia, followed by wars and blockades, slave rebellions, high taxes in England—where tea, grown in colonial India, was cheap—and finally the emancipation of slaves throughout the British empire.

Coffee was introduced to Colombia from the French West Indian islands towards the end of the eighteenth century. Small groves were established at Cúcuta, Santander. At first, most of the coffee was grown for home consumption, and any surplus was sold in the local market. The industry grew slowly, dependent as it was on pack donkeys for transportation from the interior of the country to the river and thence to the port. As roads and water transportation improved, many planters began to grow coffee, especially those who had been ruined by sugar.

At the beginning the arabica coffee was planted in lowland areas, and the quality was not good. Soon the planters discovered that plants grown in the highlands produced a much better-flavoured coffee. By the end of 1880, coffee had become the number one export, and ever since coffee planting has been a way of life for many Colombians.

In Central America, coffee was brought to Costa Rica from Cuba by a Spanish traveller named Navarro, in 1779, and from Jamaica at around the same time. The latecomers to coffee growing were Guatemala, which started to export beans in 1875, El Salvador, and Panama.

Old Coffee Houses

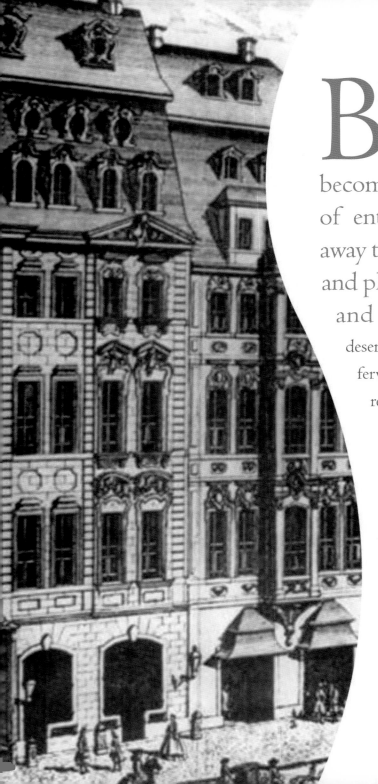

By the time coffee became accepted in the Muslim world as the drink of the faithful, coffee houses had become a way of life. They were places of entertainment where people whiled away the time listening to music, singing and playing games such as backgammon and mankala. These distractions led to the desertion of the mosques and a decrease in the religious fervour expected of strict adherents of Islam. The result was the suppression of many of the coffee houses and punishment of their customers—but in the meantime, coffee drinking had spread to Europe.

The first coffee house in England was established in 1650 at Oxford, by a Turkish Jew called Jacob. It was followed two years later by one opened by Daniel Edwards, in a tent in St Michaels Alley, Cornhill, London. On his return from Turkey, Edwards brought with him a Greek

"The first coffee ho

servant, Pasqua Rosee, who was versed in the art of roasting and preparing the brew. London's famous coffee houses—usually identified by a sign featuring a Turkish coffeepot or a sultan's head—included Will's and Peters at Covent Gardens, Jonathan's in Temple Bar, Rota's, Amsterdam and Garaway's. In these establishments, prominent men met to discuss current events, both literary and political, and to transact business. (In England, as in the Muslim countries, women were barred from entering coffee houses.) Indeed, every profession and rank had its own coffee house, as did people of different political persuasions. Would-be members of the Royal Society, for instance, frequented Tillard's and the Grecian.

Many of these coffee houses were known as 'penny universities', especially those near to universities and colleges, where an entrance fee of one penny was charged. At Rota's—essentially a debating society—secret balloting took place when the results of a debate were challenged. Anyone who wished to test the opinion of the gathering would put the question to the vote and accept the verdict, rendered by ballots dropped into a wooden box—one of several, placed in strategic places, into which customers would drop coins for the servants. These boxes bore the legend 'to insure promptness' because the coffee houses were usually so crowded that customers, including distinguished ones, had long waits for service. According to one theory, it is from the legend written on the boxes that the word 'tip' is derived.

By 1663 there were so many coffee houses in London that an Act was passed

for the better ordering and collection of duty of excise and preventing the abuse therein, express premium is made for the licensing of all coffee houses at the quarter sessions, under penalty of £5. for every month during which any person should retail coffee, chocolate or tea without having first procured such license from the magistrates.

in England was established in 1650"

In 1675 Charles II sought to close down the coffee houses, which he considered hotbeds of sedition, where customers not only gossiped but slandered persons of high status.

European coffee houses

Coffee came to Venice about 1660. At first, as in Arabia, it was treated as a medicine for all and sundry complaints. It was supposed to 'calm an impassioned man and to stimulate the quiet and reflective to deeds of passion and daring'. But its use spread so rapidly among the wealthy that by 1690 dozens of coffee houses were flourishing—and, just as they had in England, the customers gossiped and spread rumours as they sipped their coffee.

Many people thought the coffee houses contributed to all sorts of vices, and the fanatical priests asked the Pope to forbid the use of coffee, 'the Mohammedans' Satan brew'. But the Pope, having tasted it, considered it a healthy and delicious drink and thought it would be a pity to let the infidels have exclusive use of it. Thus it was duly blessed and became a holy drink for Christians as well. One of Venice's most famous cafés, the Florian, in the Piazza San Marco, was established in 1720 by Floriano Francesconi and is still in operation to this day.

Coffee houses had spread to Marseille by 1644 and began to appear in Paris in 1669, through the agency of Suliman Aga, the Turkish ambassador to the court of Louis XIV. His elaborate parties, at which this new brew was served, were exotic affairs. In his *Curiosities of Literature* (quoted in Brown Gold 1954, 11), Isaac D'Israeli describes one:

> On bended knee, the black slaves of the Ambassador, arrayed in the most gorgeous costumes, served the choicest mocha coffee poured out in saucers of gold and silver, placed on embroidered silk doilies, fringed with gold bullion, to the grand dames, who fluttered their fans with many grimaces, bending their piquant faces—berouged, bepowdered and bepatched—over the new steaming beverage.

Not long afterwards, an Armenian called Pascal sent coffee sellers through the streets of Paris with his 'petits noires'. At this stage, Parisian coffee houses catered mainly to the lower classes. In 1675, however, Etienne D'Alep opened a luxurious one in the rue des Italien and called it 'Café'. It was followed in 1689 by Café Procopé at 13 rue de l'Ancienne Commedie, the offering of François Procope, a *limonadier* who sold lemonade, spices and coffee. Both were instant successes, soon frequented by the famous. Many other entrepreneurs followed suit, and cafés opened all over Paris, becoming the haunts of artists, politicians and writers such as Voltaire, Molière, Danton, Marat and Robespierre, among others. A century later, on 12 July 1789, it was at the Café Fay that Camille Desmoulins made his stirring speech to a full house and the excited overflow crowd that stood outside. Two days later, the Bastille fell, signalling the start of the French Revolution.

In Germany, there was stiff resistance to coffee from both the beer drinkers and the beer barons. However, the women especially enjoyed the Kaffeeklatsch, where they could drink Blumchenkaffee while they talked and listened to gossip. The first coffee house was opened in Hamburg by a London merchant.

New World coffee houses

In America, small quantities of coffee beans were available as early as 1660, from the Dutch who were trading with the colonists of New Amsterdam—renamed New York four years later, when the British took possession of it. But by that time the taste of coffee had been acquired, though there was competition from local herbs and tea.

The early coffee houses that were opened in Boston, New York, Philadelphia and Baltimore did not reflect the splendour of their European counterparts; they were mere inns or taverns, with rooms for rent, that served meals as well as coffee, ale, wine, hot cocoa and tea to the sailors, merchants and soldiers who frequented them. The first person to receive a license to sell coffee was Dorothy Jones of Boston, in 1670. A few years later, Mary Gutteridge opened a coffee house—evidently, the American woman of the period was much freer than her European counterpart.

Another well-known coffee house was Boston's Green Dragon, which catered to British officers and the city's elite. New York's coffee houses were inns and taverns, where business was conducted in curtained booths. The city's most famous house was the Tontine, opened in 1792 at Wall and Water streets.

It was only during the British blockade in 1683 that Dutch and French smugglers brought in a good quantity of coffee for sale. But, as it had in England, coffee remained a drink for well-to-do people. Tea, which was much cheaper, had long been the favoured hot beverage. The Americans became firm coffee drinkers after the Boston Tea Party in 1773, when Samuel Adams and 150 patriots, disguised as Mohawk Indians, boarded the British East India Company's tea-laden vessels and threw overboard 342 chests of tea, signalling the beginning of the colonial tax resistance that led to the American War of Independence.

TheJamaican Coffee Story

Gabriel de Clieu had planted the first arabica coffee plant in Martinique in 1717. By 1728, Sir Nicholas Lawes, the governor of Jamaica, was able to acquire not only coffee beans but plants from Martinique. They were planted on his estate at Temple Hall, St Andrew.

At the same time, a planter from Vere, in the parish of Clarendon, also imported some beans from Martinique. Only one plant grew from this batch of beans. When it began to bear, the demand for the beans was so great that he received 'a bit o' berry' or fourpence, a considerable sum in those days.

Encouragement Act 5 of George II was passed in 1732, four years after the introduction of coffee, 'to encourage growth of coffee in his Majestys plantation in America'. This it did by reducing the duty for coffee imported from Jamaica from two shillings to one shilling sixpence, the first case of preferential treatment in the Empire.

"Coffee cultivation began

The growing of coffee was promoted actively by the House of Assembly. Not only would coffee production increase the wealth of the country; it was practical, because, whereas sugar cane was grown in the hot lowlands, coffee was best grown on the steep slopes of the mountains, where cane would not grow. Cultivation would also enable the opening up of the mountainous lands of the interior to more white settlers, as John Ellis noted in 1774 (217):

> as the lesser planters might be able to subsist by raising this and other small articles of West India produce, their numbers would increase and add to the defense and security of several islands. For especially since the cultivation of such articles would attend with no greater labour than what Europeans are capable of enduring without any peril to their lives.

Coffee cultivation began in the foothills of the St. Andrew mountains and gradually extended into the steep interior of the eastern Blue Mountains, eventually reaching the highest point, the Peak, at 7,402 feet.

The first recorded export of Jamaican coffee was in 1737, when 83,400 pounds were sold to agents in England. But production fluctuated, dropping as low as 24,800 pounds in 1746. No doubt this was a result of the duty imposed on coffee, which was kept high to protect the British East India Company's growing tea market and because of the worsening financial situation in Britain. The market was also being flooded by coffee from the French islands, especially Haiti (then St. Domingue), as well as the Dutch product, which depressed the price. If it had not been for the sale of coffee to the American market before 1783, coffee production in the British islands, including Jamaica, would probably have ceased.

...be foothills of the St. Andrew mountains..."

After the American War of Independence, the duty on coffee was reduced by two-thirds. This stimulated production, and new fields were laid out and planted. But the most crucial factor that led to the boom years of coffee production in Jamaica—from 1790, when 2,783,800 pounds were produced, to 1814, with production of 34,045,600 pounds—was the slave uprising in Haiti in 1789. Haiti was at that time the world's largest producer of coffee, exporting some 77 million pounds per year. This huge production ceased overnight, and all and sundry scrambled to get hold of whatever coffee was available. Good prices, of course, led to the expansion of production.

Jamaica also welcomed fleeing Haitian planters, many of whom were skilled in the growing of coffee. The most famous of them was Pierre-Joseph Laborie, a lawyer and coffee farmer who served on the *Conseils superieur* under the British occupation of Haiti, and who published, in London, his book *The Coffee Planter of Saint Domingo*.

Between 1790 and 1805, Jamaica enjoyed a steady increase in coffee production, with rapid expansion in every parish. This occurred despite a parallel increase in duty during Britain's wars with France—rising above its former high in 1806. But in that year, not only was the slave trade abolished by Britain—which would have long-term implications for labour—but other international events placed a great burden on Jamaica's coffee farmers. Napoleon imposed a blockade on British goods entering Europe during the second round of the Anglo-French war, between 1807 and 1814, which was known as the Continental System. Trade with the United States was curtailed as a result of the American Embargo Act of 1807–09 and the war of 1812–14 between the United States and Britain.

A rare survival of letters between a coffee farmer named John Mackeson and his brothers in England, William and Harry, describes his daily life and experience during his residence in the

30

Setting the Coffee Seeds

island, from 1807 to 1819. John Mackeson's property actually belonged to his wife, Olive, and although he could have sold it for some £10,000, her family did not wish him to sell. In 1805, just before his marriage, in England, he wrote:

> I have just had a long conversation with Mr Wyllys, the brother of Olive, and he has agreeably surprised me with the information that the estates in the west (Jamaica) produced from £1,000 pounds to £1,200 pounds yearly. That added to what I possess—do you think it will be sufficient inducement for me to settle in this country?

On July 13, a day after they were married, he wrote from Bath:

> The Blue Mountains I always entertained an idea were not in jeopardy; and the disgraceful retreat of the combined fleet from Martinique now places them beyond a doubt in full serenity. I most sincerely hope Nelson will overtake them not withstanding there is so great a disparity in numbers. I anticipate much pleasure from the news of a glorious victory. Oh! what a thorn it will be in the side of the renowned Corsican. I would give a trifle to be near him when he receives the intelligence of the glorious achievements of his boasted navy.
>
> Pitt requires at this moment something of this kind to keep him from sinking. The Fates have never yet deserted him when at a pinch. The secession of the Addingtons will I fear nearly throw him into a minority. He is certainly a wonderful man, but I much fear he must fall at last.

March 1807 finds Mackeson in Jamaica, living at his brother-in-law's sugar plantation, Mount Lebanus, in the eastern parish of St. Thomas. On May 27, 1807, he wrote to his brother William in England:

Unloading Cherry Ripe Coffee at Central Factory

I am in hopes to improve the estate as I shall immediately plant coffee—that is, if I can settle amicably with the person who disputes the land with me. He has expressed a wish to compromise the business, which I most certainly shall in preference to going to law. I have an excellent gang of Negroes, which I shall now employ on my own property, which has been totally neglected.

In a postscript dated June 11, 1807, he added:

Yesterday I entered into my thirty-first year, which I hope will terminate prosperously, though I must confess the times and appearances prognosticate otherwise. I allude more particularly to the pernicious effects the abolition of the slave trade will have on the minds of our Negroes. I very much fear we shall have much trouble to keep them in subjection—indeed, I shudder when I think what may be the consequences. Only recall to mind the massacres of Santo Domingo. We have reason to be alarmed. However, should it please God to avert so great an evil as an insurrection, I shall still be tolerably well off, though numbers will be ruined. But if it should take place, I am a lost man, and the country in all probability will be lost to the mother country, as the forces are very inadequate to the defense of the island.

On March 4, 1808, he wrote to his brother Harry. By this time, Mackeson and Olive had a daughter.

The present times bear a most gloomy aspect, truly discouraging to us West Indians. Numbers in this country must be ruined; many are already so. However those who are able to bear up through the impending difficulties will reap the benefits hereafter.

Another letter that survives is dated March 30, 1811, and is to his brother William. It was written from his pen (livestock farm) near Kingston.

Pulping and Washing Operations

I know not how you bear up against the times in your part of the world, but in this we are drooping wretchedly, and unless some change takes place we must sink altogether. My plantation bids fair for a good crop; but what signifies? there is no sale for the commodity—I have my last year's crop on hand.

Mrs M. and her two little ones are, thank God, well. We shall leave this quarter on the 7th of next month for Blue Mountains, from whence I will write you at some length; but at present I partake of the general affection of melancholy that I cannot sit long to write.

Almost exactly a year later, on March 29, 1812, he wrote from his plantation:

I wish I could get back again. I am now become fixed in this island, and must rise and fall with it. I observe what you and Harry recommend in your letter, and could it have been accomplished would have done it two years ago: but really there is now very few people in the island that can command £1,000 sterling. There are no purchasers. I allowed my factor in February to obtain judgement against me for £3,432–6s–3d currency (1.8 stg). This is a large sum to be cleared off; and there has been no possibility of late to effect any sales of coffee, although we are now led to expect that it is improving in price. Should so fortunate an event take place, I have now by me about 80,000 pounds of coffee, if not more. I am told last week 75s. a cwt. was refused in Kingston: if I had mine there, I would not have refused 60s. There can be no doubt if a vent can be found for coffee, that it will again fetch good prices, though I imagine nothing equal to what it has done—say 100s per cwt., which will pay very well. I propose selling mine in this country.

Should colonial produce sell well, Negroes will again become very valuable. I have now 98 slaves, which I would not take less than £10,000 sterling for; and as they are coming much in request they will of course increase in value.

I have attached to my breeding pen about 1,500 pounds of horses and mules, and 1,600 of cattle, which are increasing and doing well. My pen in Liguanea and houses in Kingston I can get £5,000 for.

Loading Wet Parchment Coffee for Delivery to Finishing Works

I have now given you an insight as to what I am possessed of, independent of the plantation, pen lands, new land, buildings attached, which would be very considerable, but I cannot in the present time say what.

Negroes	£14,000	currency
stock	£3,100	"
Pen & houses	£5,000	"
80,000 lb coffee say 60s. per cwt which is very low	£2,400	"
	————	
	£24,500	"
From which I should have to deduct about for the judgement etc	£4,000	
	————	
which would leave a balance of	£20,500	"
independent of the plantation etc. The above I think a very low valuation.		

I expect from the general appearance of the trees that my crop will be about 50,000 pounds. As to living cheap, we cannot be in a better place than we are. We sacrifice everything to economy. We have

Mechanical Loading of Dried Parchment Coffee on Barbecue

no society whatever. Our principal expenses are clothing, and salt provisions for the Negroes, and our wine; and the whole does not amount to £1,000 pounds per annum, to meet which:

Next year 50,000

lb at 60s cwt.	£ 1,500	(currency)
Mules	£ 320	"
Rent of pen and houses	£ 520	"
	_____	
making	£ 2,340	"

But recollect I calculate on effecting sales of coffee. I shall now quit the subject, and hope that next time I write to give more favourable accounts.

Things were so bad that I considered planting castor oil and, to make matters worse, war was declared with the United States on the 18th June 1812.

In August, Mackeson was in Kingston, as his wife was expecting another baby, and on August 2 he wrote:

I shall be most happy when it is over that I may get back again to Blue Mountains, for independent of the heavy expense attending our stay here, it is most painful to my feelings to be a daily witness, the unparalleled distress of every of every class of people.

However, he was still in Kingston in December, for on December 16, 1812, he wrote to his brothers the news that 'a violent storm—possibly a hurricane—has destroyed the greatest part

Cup Testing to Ensure the Highest Quality

of my crop of coffee'. In a letter to Harry dated March 19, 1813, he seemed to be in a more cheerful mood:

I am now very busy getting my coffee down for market. As yet there is no sale for it in the country. I shall therefore (by the fleet which sails the latter end of April) send from 50 to 60 tierces (800 lbs per tierce) to England—all that I can get ready by that time. Should there be any speculators in the market here (which I think is very probable soon) to give a fair price, I shall prefer selling here. I think the quantity I have ought to enable me to clear my heavy debt to West and Fowler. I shall be most happy to get once more clear; and if I can get a purchaser, I will get rid of all my property here. I shall however, continue to push them as much as possible at the best of times. They are very precarious in their returns; for instance, last year instead of 60,000, I only got 15,000—a dreadful loss.

The war with America still continues, though I believe they begin to be tired with as our offensive measures begin to operate and to convince them of their insignificance. I understand that the question of war or peace was debated in Congress, when the latter was carried by a great majority and commissioners appointed to wait upon Sir John Borlase Warren (British naval commander) to bring it about. To which there cannot be any difficulty, provided they admit the right to Search. This they must do if they want peace. It was rather unfortunate their taking two of our frigates in the outset. I hear that two of theirs have been taken and carried into Plymouth. The reverses of their Friend Bony will probably hasten the peace.

By March 1814, the British Navy's successes against the French were generating much optimism that the war would soon be over; in fact, it ended at Waterloo in 1815. On March 9, 1814, Mackeson wrote to Harry thus:

Most sincerely do I participate in the general joy occasioned by the reverses of the detested Corsican, it has been the salvation of the poor West Indians. Two years more, and I should probably have sunk, as many have already done, never to have recovered again. It has now turned out fortunate that I kept my coffee in store, although in so doing it has become very inferior.

Hulling and Grading Operations

Because the coffee market was depressed as a result of the wars and embargoes, Mackeson had replaced some of his coffee fields with castor oil (castor beans). When the tide of the Anglo-French war turned in favour of the British—although Napoleon was not defeated until the Battle of Waterloo in 1815—the coffee market bounced back. Mackeson wrote:

> I—unfortunately as it has now turned out—threw up the coffee, which will of course throw me back for two years at least. I shall, however, I think be able to muster the next crop about 30 tierces good coffee, which will, I trust, meet all contingencies. In 1815 I shall have a small field of young coffee, and expect 40 tierces at least. In 1816 it is impossible to say what I may make, as it in great measure depends upon how much land I can get into coffee this year; but I think it will be sufficient to give me something handsome.

John Mackeson apparently left Jamaica with his family at some time during 1816 or 1817. His last surviving letter from Jamaica, written in 1816, displays his enthusiasm for the war with the United States. He wrote:

> The Yankees are now coming off second best, and begin to cry loudly for peace. I hope they will be well trounced before it is granted them. They thought they could have starved us poor West Indians; but we never have been better supplied with everything than since the rupture. Besides, it has taught us to look to our own resources, and we find them adequate. Thus instead of injury, they have done us a service: we can now live within ourselves at but a trifling expense.

It appears that by 1819 Mackeson was still in possession of his coffee plantation, although now an absentee, receiving some £3,000 per annum—in those days an ample income to support a comfortable life.

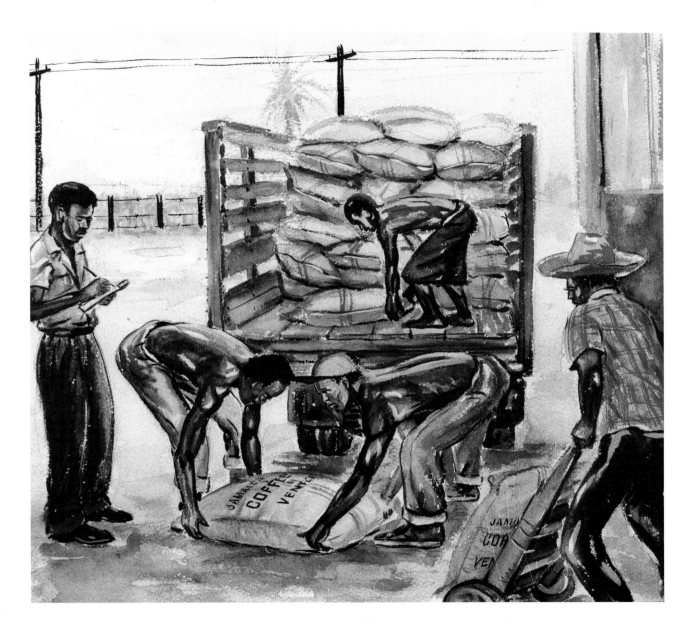

On the Way to the Wharf

45

The decline of production

Following the peak of coffee production in 1814, totalling some 34,045,600 pounds—the figure no doubt reflects the release of coffee that was stored over some years and could not be sold by the planters—there was a steady decline in production from 1815 on. This was primarily caused by the Continental System, which was in place from 1806 to 1814. Many coffee planters became bankrupt, though they tried to salvage what they could. Another factor that had a long-lasting effect on coffee production in the eastern parishes was extensive soil erosion. Between 1800 and 1805, at least 56 plantations were abandoned because of soil erosion and infertile soil.

Between 1820 and 1830 there was stiff competition from Haiti, Ceylon and Brazil—where the slave trade continued on a massive scale. The export of coffee from Jamaica was now at 22,257,000 pounds. Nevertheless, planting continued.

The Middleton Papers

A valuable collection of records and letters was preserved from the estates of the Dukes of Buckingham and Chandos and is now housed in the Huntington Library, forming the Stowe Collection (Americana), which includes the dukes' coffee plantations, Middleton and Merrymans Field, and the Hope Estate, a sugar plantation at Papine.

The coffee plantations of Merrymans Field (1,000 acres) and Middleton (300 acres) were situated along the Hope River, in St Andrew, at elevations of 2,500 feet and above. The Middleton

To all Parts of the World

plantation came up for sale in 1832, as correspondence between Richard Barrett and the Duke confirms.

Hope—ApriI 8, 1832

It is reported to me that Middleton will be sold next month to pay the lawyers bills. I shall take care, if Your Grace is the purchaser that the title is good. The price will be much less than I supposed when I first had the [?] to open the subject for Your Grace.

27 March 1833

To John Robson

Dear Sirs,

The Duke of Buckingham requests that you will see Mr Humphrys on the subject of bills drawn on his Grace by his Agent in Jamaica for £900. One of them has reached His Grace for £500, having been presented by Mr Jurkombe [?] upon your acceptance.

The bills are drawn for the purchase of Middleton and the [?] letter from W. Campbell to Mr Duye [?] and myself will show the total amount of purchase money [?] will be about £4350 from which £600 will be deducted, being the value of the coffee in hand. Having had some conversation with you on the subject of Middleton, I have only to add that his Grace is desirous of completing the purchase and he is willing to [?] with the security required by Mr Humphrys and to settle Middleton on the Marquis of Chandos in the same manner in which other property of his Grace is settled on the [?] Marquis.

I must express my own hope that the Marquis of Chandos will write [?] with his Grace in the necessary security to Mr Humphrys so that Mr Humphrys maybe induced to [?] money to meet this purchase and I be relieved of the responsibility I have incurred in directing the [?] to be made according to his Grace's commands.

I shall be ready to explain to the Marquis the advantage of the [?] of Middleton to his family Estates in Jamaica should his [?] require information on the subject.

signed. Rich Barrett.

The following is a report made by an agent, Mr William Barron, who was sent out to Jamaica by the duke to report on the state of his properties.

2nd Feb. 1843

My Dear Duke,

I avail myself of the earliest opportunity to acquaint Your Grace that I arrived safely at this Island in the evening of the 30th January, after a passage of 28 days from Falmouth via Corunia, Madeira, Antigua and St Thomas on the way out.

Having understood that Mr G. [Gordon] was in Kingston, I called upon him on the morning after my arrival, but found he had gone into the country for the afternoon. I have left your Grace's letter with my card for him and he called upon me yesterday morning at half past 9.

In a letter dated February 16, 1843, Mr Barron remarked on the low ebb of agricultural interest and how difficult it was to procure labour. Many properties were up for sale 'but scarcely any offer made and if so at a ruinously low rate'. He continued:

> I am quite certain that if matters continue much longer in this present state, the cultivation of these colonies will be abandoned in a few years and be augmented ... in the neighbouring Spanish colonies of Cuba and Puerto Rico either of which can make sugar and coffee enough to supply the whole world. ... I hope to be able to get some shaddocks and other fruits that will keep to go home and also the seeds and plants opportunately by merchant vessels will now be offered every week for some months.

Mr Barron's report on Middleton and Merrymans Hill follows.

Middleton

This plantation, containing by recent survey 300 acres is situated about 3 1/2 miles NNW from the Hope on the western side of the River [Hope River] and Merrymans Hill, the mountain road from the valley to the military post of Newcastle passing thro' it. It is cultivated solely in coffee, its mountainous situation not admitting of its being put to any other purpose. The quality of the coffee it produces is extremely good and its eastern aspect is favourable for the growth of that plant in the highest degree.

Produce

The greater part of the coffee Trees on this property are in good bearing, the remainder require to be renewed and indeed the cultivation will be considerably extended when the plants just put in at Merrymans Hill come into bearing.
I find the joint produce from these two properties for 3 years ending in 1842 to have been in—

Middleton Coffee Estate, St. Andrew, c 1850 (Lloyd)

1840	54 (tierces) I tierce = 800 lbs.
1841	73 "
1842	17 "

In all, 144 tierces giving an average of 48 tierces which at a moderate estimate of £40 stg a time gives £1920 a year or from the whole period £5760.

I find the expenditure for the same period (exclusive of repairs and the quota of rent—say £400 p.a.) to have been as follows

Coffee	5760.0.0
Average for 3 years	
£1093.3.10	
1840	£1060.11.1
1841	1079.5.7
1842	1139.14.11
	_____
	3279.11.7 say 3280.0.0
	_____
	2480.0.0
Proportions of 3 yrs rent	1200 0.0
	_____
Profit for 3 years	£1280.0
	_____

Labour

The number of slaves formerly on Middleton Estate was 226 viz. 108 males and 118 females, of all ages.

The average amount of labour during the last 3 years, taken from the wages actually paid was 13863 days per annum equal at the rate of 208 working days a year (to about) by efficient labourers.

Memorandum of information on Hope and Middleton [*Note: This section of the report was written in two columns, with questions in the left column and responses in the right. In the interests of space and ease of reading, it is presented here with questions in italics followed by answers in roman type.*]

What should you consider value of each estate to be at present, & whether by the greater outlay they could be rendered more valuable?
The sugar estate including Merrymans Hill I consider worth £10,000.0. The coffee property with the works I think about £300.0

Is there any probability of letting the water of the Hope River for the use of the garrison, and upon which term annually?
The water from the Hope not required for the garrison. Papine Estate supplies it. Kingston to buy the Hope water for the use of the town. Garrison supplied by Papine Estate £400.0 p.a.

Middleton Bldgs – works in good order – but requiring shingling (£150) – overseers house and huts good but require shingling (£100) also. Repairs and other costs altogether £350.

Is the Middleton Estate capable of sending more coffee than Litherts [?]
The present fields at Middleton have no coffee land to extend the crops. But some young coffee has been lately put in at Merrymans Hill which will extend them. But from the cold nature of the soil and climate it would take 5 or 6 years to come into bearing.

Will it be advantageous to dispose of more lots of ground to government for military posts?
It would certainly be very advantageous.

Does the estate possess great facilities for shipping its produce?
The produce is shipped from Kingston—ships belonging to individuals.

To what parties in England are the produce of the Estates chiefly consigned?
Since Mr Gordon became lessee to William Morrice of London since deceased.

Is there any wood timber on the Estates; if there be, how is it chiefly disposed of? State quantity of value.
Sufficient for the purpose of the Estates during crop time and kept for that purpose. (None sold. little wood at either estate).

In what state are the roads on & in the neighbourhood of the property?
T h e   roads are good hard bottom (to Hope). The road to Middleton is merely a bridle path in the mountains and very rugged in many places.

What quantity of pasture ground is there at Hope and Middleton— Is it in good order?
300 acres on the Hope, without any fence and will cost a large sum to fence it. At Middleton there are no pastures hardly fit even for a mule (owing to the steepness of the Hills).

Of what class are the dissenters on the estates chiefly composed?
Church of England, Wesleyans, Baptists and London church missionary.

Is any articifial horse manure used.
None.

Are the labourers upon the estates considered effective.
Very effective—but on Hope very unwilling; on Middleton (pretty) well disposed.

Is there any (or many) unemployed, particularly labourers residing upon the estates?
On the Hope there are more unemployed—than employed—and great difficulty in obtaining labour from the proximity to town; and great facility in selling fruit and provisions.
[Company formed to supply water to Kingston not included here]

How many days labour were expended on the Hope and Middleton estates during the last year? Stating the amount for each respectively.
Hope 1842—30,250 days labour at 1/- [1 shilling] average. Middleton—average for 3 years at 1/- p/day—annually, 13,860.

What amount of annual labour would these estates respectively require, in order to be cultivated to the full extent of production of which they are capable?
Equal to about 84,000 labourers for 1 day for Hope and 18,600 for Middleton. Hope = 400 labourers 4 days a week. Middleton = 90 labourers 4 days per week.

Would such amount of labour employed in the existing state of wages with a sufficiently remunerative result to the cultivator?
It is very doubtful (much would depend upon the Seasons and the price of product in Europe).

What is the average number of days' work in the week (or its equivalent in task work) performed by the labourer now?

Four days (labourers like every Friday and Saturday for their own purposes).

Does any disposition generally exist among the labourers to exact more than the ordinary rate of wages during croptime or any period of emergency?

They take advantage of every opportunity to raise the wages particularly in crop time and in planting canes.

What are the average annual expenses to the cultivator of these estates, respectively under the several heads of wages of labour, salaries and the various other outlays?

Middleton:

Labour exp.	£ 693.3.2-1/2
Premium	5.3.2
duties	14.10.11
tollage	9.7.3
taxes	96.13.4
supplies	100.0.0
wharfage	5.8.4
mules	35.0.0
casualities	30.0.0
salaries	93I0.8

£1083.6.9-1/2

(this is exclusive of repairs to buildings and rent.)

Merrymans Hill

This property is situated about 3 miles distant from the Hope in a North easterly direction. It is bounded on the North by "Newcastle" and "Cold Spring" Estates—on the east by "Pleasant Hill" and "Newtons"—on the south by "Industry" and on the West by the "Hopewell" and Middleton plantations from which it is divided by a ravine and the Hope River. It is entirely situated in the western side of a very steep Mountain, and can only be used for planting coffee. Its extent, by the nearest approach that can be made by survey, is 961 acres. (p. 48)

In his report of February 1843 to the Duke of Chandos, Barron reported on the state of Middleton.

From here we were obliged to proceed to Middleton which is situated 3 miles further up the Mountain. Here we were obliged to proceed on mules, the path being very steep and ragged, and so narrow that 2 mules can scarcely pass each other. The path winds round the hill on the side of the ravines in some places 200 feet deep, at the bottom of which flows the Hope river. Middleton is situated amidst very wild and picturesque scenery and the temperature is considerably lower than at Hope. Coffee picking is going on just now and Mr Gordon tells me that he expects to have a tolerable crop this year. Here is an overseers House, watermill, drying yard and stores in very fair order. I saw in the buildings a European named Thomas Bill who told me he came from Eaton near Avington, and is one of a lot of labourers sent out some years back from that neighbourhood, only 2 or 3 of them survive however, the remainder having died from giving way to irregular and intemporate [*sic*] habits. Near this plantation is the new military post called Newcastle, 90 acres of this part in Middleton lands and Mr Gordon has valued it at £15. per acre to Government, which is considered a good price, especially as I should say that the land is very poor and not capable of cultivation. All produce from this estate is obliged to be brought down to town on the backs of mules which makes the carriage expensive from the number of animals to be kept, and the mountains being too steep to allow of animal grazing. ...

From all enquiries which I have made here, I have no doubt of Mr G. being a very respectable and substantial man. He is considered to be a complete practical planter having been engaged in that pursuit about 35 years. He owns 2 sugar and 2 coffee plantations, and I understand that with these, and those which he rents and acts as agent for, he represents in all 45 estates. He is agent, or as it is here called Attorney, for Lord Carringtone, Sir Alexander Grant, Lord Seaford and various other individuals of rank and status. I am therefore inclined to think that your Grace could not find a safer or more substantial lessee in this place than Mr Gordon.

Having thus given your Grace an outline of my proceedings during the few days I have been here, I shall conclude by assuring you that I will proceed immediately to a more methodical inquiry, and keep your grace duly informed on my movements and progress from time to time.

I have put the collection of seeds and plants in [train?] and will properly attend to your wishes on the subject of them as also of the fruits and preserves.

Map

... there is no map of Middleton, but Mr Gordon thinks he could get one made for about £150. Would your Grace wish to go to this expense?
I think that my best plan will be to defray the expenses of the above object as well as any of these that may be available by granting Bills in my house in London, for which your Grace can make provisions upon hearing from me. This will be better than my drawing direct on you.
I have the honour to be my Lord Duke, Your Grace's most ob. of faithful servant.
W. Barron.

To His Grace,
The Duke of Buckingham & Chandos, K.G.
ARTICLES SENT BY SHIP "SCOTSMAN", February 1843

5 pots preserve ginger	20 lbs
2 pots preserve limes	6 lbs
2 pots preserve green sweetmeats	6 lbs

2 pots preserve guava	6 lbs in a cask
2 pots preserved green tamarind jams	6 lbs
12 bottles pickles	
12 bottles castor oil	in a cask
12 bottles cashew nuts (doubtful)	
1 box cassava cakes	
1 box coffee (from Middleton Estates)	
1 cwt yams	

N.B. The cassava cakes are somewhat like the oat cake in appearance, but thinner & much more delicate in flavour. They should be dressed thus—first buttered and then toasted on a grid-iron—they are esteemed a great delicacy.

The yam should be dressed as follows—Baked in a strong oven until thoroughly done, then cut open lengthwise, the contents dressed with butter that has been corned or slightly salted, the same way as mashed potatoes, and then replaced in the husk or shell of the root, and braised in a little dutch oven opposite a brisk fire.

I have given the mode of dressing both these articles always adopted here, & which I believe to be the best.
W.B.

P.S. I have written to Barbados to have a few dozen bottles of the best Falernum sent from there to Your Grace. It is an exceedingly agreeable beverage in warm weather, taken either alone or with water.

Letter to His Grace 20th March 1843

... I have been occupied since my last communication of the 16th February in prosecuting my inquiries and visiting the estates and I find that I have acquired as much practical information at present to enable me to report upon all points necessary for your information & guidance as I should require if I were to remain here 6 months.

... I venture to offer, that the lease of the properties intended for the late Mr Morrice should be transferred to Mr Gordon. I shall in my report afford good and sufficient reasons for offering this advice; at present I have only time to say, that under existing circumstances, and even under the most favourable prospects that can be anticipated for this colony for several years to come, I consider Your Grace to have by far the best of the bargain in receiving from Mr Gordon a rent of £1200 std.p.a.

W. Barron

A letter from Middleton dated February 19, 1856, written by J.G. Gore, indicates a new manager who is reporting to Messrs. Map & Co. on the state of the estate.

Messrs. S. Map & Co.
Gentlemen,
According to request I beg to forward for your information the annual report of the present state of this plantation under my management.
I am Gentlemen
Your Humble Servant

J.R. Gore

The extent of the present coffee pieces in this plantation are five in No. and by names, Titus, Black grove, Naylors, Currati Hill and Newton; comprising in all 90 or 100 acres in good and indifferent coffee trees with many patches bare.

The best and furthest field is Newton and the poorest is Currati Hill—These fields have been regularly kept in a planter like order, since I have been in charge of the property—is now in good cultivation, and promises to give an adequate return; Most of these pieces have suffered to go out by allowing the labourers to convert them from time to time into provision grounds, which cannot be now redeemed. As it is essential to increase the crops and seeing the importance of such, I have during the year had lands in the extent of 40, odd acres cut, cleaned and planted in coffee, which to the present time is doing as well as could be expected. These new fields will be a great acquisition to the plantation in time, its situation is continuous to 4 of the other fields.

In this report I trust I have given you an Epitome of the present state of the plantation, and thanking you for your consideration.
I am resp.
Yrs. J.R. Gore
P.S. Your of the 11th came to hand on the 15th which accounts for the lateness of this.

As John Bigelow, an American, sailed into Kingston Harbour, his eyes swept over the Blue Mountains in the distance, and he wrote in his *Jamaica in 1850*: 'Our eyes were directed ... on the mountains, to the abandoned coffee estates, belonging to the bankrupt Duke of Chandos.'

By 1853, both properties of Hope and Middleton were leased to the Reverend William David Morrice and Joseph Gardner for ten years. Thus ends the correspondence. The property was probably later sold and subdivided. In 1960 the overseer's house and barbecues, comprising 17 acres, were owned by an Englishwoman. In 1970 the property was further divided, along the line of a bridle path running by the Hope River. The overseer's house (which was in fair condition as late as the 1960s but has since been replaced by a wooden structure) with 14 acres was sold to a Mr Cramm. The three remaining acres along the river, with the three coffee barbecues, were sold to Fred and Norma Benghiat in their company name, Antikhana Limited.

The post-emancipation period

In 1799 there were 686 coffee plantations in operation with 30,000 acres in cultivation. By 1847, according to Douglas Hall, writing in the magazine *Free Jamaica*, 'since emancipation 465 coffee plantations had been abandoned and the works broken up'.

Small peasant farmers took over the cultivation of coffee. Lack of financing and equipment to properly process the coffee resulted in a decline in quality. By 1942, 90 per cent of the 30,000 farmers held between one and 25 acres. But total production was a dismal 5,305,300 pounds. D. Morris (1887) wrote, 'I fear unless something is done by the coffee planters and coffee merchants to improve and maintain the general character of Jamaican coffee, its name and position in the markets of the world, will before long, be severely compromised.'

During and after the second World War, coffee production was at its lowest, reacting to low prices and the growth of the banana industry. In a letter dated January 25, 1944, A.J. Wakefield, then Inspector General of Agriculture for the West Indies, stated:

At present, the greater part of the coffee cultivation is in a state of neglect and at the same time there are some considerable areas of land in upper and lower Manchester suitable for extension in coffee especially in the Christiana area, where areas formerly under banana have been rendered unsuitable for cultivation in that crop because of the spread of Panama disease. Coffee should also be selected to replace pimento on suitable lands in those areas where this crop has been destroyed by rust.

The Coffee Industry Board

In 1945, Wakefield's report 'The Rehabilitation of the Coffee Industry in Jamaica' formed the basis for the establishment of the Jamaica Coffee Board. Under the Coffee Industry Regulation Law of 1948, the Coffee Board was established in 1950 with wide powers to regulate the industry, undertaking to process and market the coffee. By the 1950s, there was marked improvement in the quality of the coffee though not in its production, despite the distribution of some three million seedlings between 1945 and 1954. Processing was done by central pulperies located in the coffee areas, nine owned by the Coffee Board and three privately owned. However, the final processing and grading was done at the central works in Kingston. By 1960 the Board's monopoly extended to the issuing of licences to coffee roasters, stipulating that all coffee supplies must be obtained through the Board.

The 1970s saw a significant shift in the marketing of Jamaican coffee, away from the traditional market in England—especially Jamaica Blue Mountain®, which made up about 10 per cent of the total coffee production. Japanese coffee importers began buying Jamaica Blue Mountain® coffee on a long-term basis, paying a much better price than could be had on the world market. Ninety per cent of the Jamaica Blue Mountain® coffee, and almost the same percentage of the lowland coffee, was then sold to Japan. Loans for coffee expansion and resuscitation—especially after the 1988 hurricane—have been made to the board by the Japanese over the years, starting in 1974 with two loans by the Ataka and Company, one of Japan's largest trading companies. The Japanese have also become involved in the growing of coffee in the island.

Deregulation

From the time of its establishment in 1950, the Coffee Board had exercised a monopoly on the purchase and sale of all Jamaican coffee. This was intended to ensure that the coffee was properly processed, graded and tested to international standards and that all sales, both local and abroad, were carried out through the board. The method was highly successful in producing high-grade coffees, both lowland and Jamaica Blue Mountain® coffees, but production remained low.

To stimulate production, the industry was deregulated in 1983. The government's Policy Paper on Coffee states:

> The incremental production of growers (using 1980/81 crop as the base year) will be the prime consideration of the CIB in the deregulation of the coffee industry as the intention is not to disturb Jamaica's traditional markets, but rather to increase export production and returns to the growers, and to maximise foreign exchange earnings.

Licences were to be granted to 'approved growers'—growers who produced a minimum of 10,000 boxes of cherry coffee a year, a production that would be certified by the board. An approved grower would, in addition to marketing his own coffee, be allowed to purchase coffee for export. However, he would have to specify the farm and area from which the coffee would be bought and how it would be processed and marketed. The deregulation of the processing of coffee meant that an approved grower could apply to process his own coffee, provided that he 'has satisfied the board that the proper facilities to process cherry coffee to parchment or clean beans will be established'.

The board would also grant a dealer's licence to an approved grower to sell locally and export coffee 'provided he can meet the conditions set by the Board for selling locally and exporting coffee'. To ensure that quality was maintained, the board stated: 'The approved processor must have each export shipment checked by a quality control inspector of the Board before his export licence is endorsed by the Board certifying that the shipment is of exportable quality.'

On the 1st August 2004, the Coffee Industry Board was separated into two distinct bodies, each assuming separate functions. The Coffee Industry Board became the regulatory body whereas the Wallenford Coffee Company Limited took over the commercial activities and related assets. The Coffee Industry Board therefore, no longer owns pulperies or processing and grading facilities.

Jamaica Blue Mountain®
Coffee

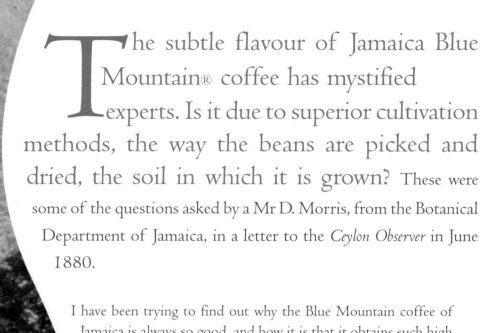

The subtle flavour of Jamaica Blue Mountain® coffee has mystified experts. Is it due to superior cultivation methods, the way the beans are picked and dried, the soil in which it is grown? These were some of the questions asked by a Mr D. Morris, from the Botanical Department of Jamaica, in a letter to the *Ceylon Observer* in June 1880.

I have been trying to find out why the Blue Mountain coffee of Jamaica is always so good, and how it is that it obtains such high prices as compared with the fine and highly cultivated coffee of Ceylon. Is the coffee grown here a peculiar variety of C. Arabica? or is there something in the soil and climate which promotes the larger formation of the essential oils and secretions in the fragrant beans? Whatever it is, it cannot be in the superior cultivation, the more rational treatment of the crop, or the greater care in curing. The only cultivation which the estates here receive consists in a rough hoe-weeding, once or twice a year, with no pruning, except what the hoe does, no system of drainage, no terracing, and, as I mentioned before, no manuring! It is true that on one or two estates a higher style of cultivation is being inaugurated, but, as a rule, coffee cultivation in Jamaica cannot compare at all with what is being done in Ceylon. It may seem strange to a Ceylon Planter, but all the work of pulping curing and

'I have been trying to find out

preparing the coffee is done here on the estates by the superintendent or overseer, and when the coffee is sent down to Kingston it is ready for shipment and immediately put in barrels. This system, and the absence of large coffee-curing establishments, must necessarily increase the cost of curing, etc., but it appears to have been pursued here from time immemorial, and planters appear to like it.

The crop of the last season was sold, in some instances, at 130s. per cwt. I had the pleasure, the other day of visiting Radnor plantation. I found it a good type of Jamaican estate, most of which have been in cultivation for more than a century and a half. In some places the trees were poor and "sticky", but wherever the soil has been preserved, and especially in the "bosoms", the trees were looking healthy and strong. In spite of "no manure" in spite of "mammoty" weeding for generations, these trees were bearing good crops and moreover, the producer is able to obtain prices which Ceylon planters must envy.

Owing to the large areas nominally included under one estate, the different "coffee-fields" are sometimes two or three miles away from the works, lying in "bosoms" of the hills, and only visited for the occasional "hoeing" and picking of the crop. Out of a nominal acreage of 1,000 acres often there are only 260 to 200 acres, and sometimes only about 60 to 80 acres, under cultivation. The other parts are in "raccinate" (jungle), or so steep that owing to "breakaways" and rocks it is impossible to cultivate them. This gives a Jamaican coffee estate a very patchy appearance, and as cinchona has not yet been taken up generally by planters, the uncultivated areas greatly exceed those cultivated. Much more might be done with the suitable coffee lands if a regulated system of nurseries were established and plants put out with greater care. At present new lands are planted up with "suckers" (seedlings) found under the trees. These are pulled up with little or no care, even when they have six or eight primaries and after being carried in bundles on heads exposed to the full rays of the sun are put in holes, and allowed to take their chance without shade or shelter. It is strange to hear such plants called "suckers", but that is the orthodox term for them here, and it is on such plants that Jamaica planters entirely depend for their supplies and for planting up. I was much puzzled the other day with a remark made me by a planter respecting these said "suckers". I asked why these self-sown plants were called "suckers", when evidently they were nothing of the kind. I suggested "seedlings" as an appropriate term. I was told:

Blue Mountian coffee of Jamaica is so good"

"No, no, they are not seedlings: a sucker does not become a seedling till it is crowned." This was still worse, and I had to give it up.

With regard to the absence of nurseries and the planting up of land by weakly sown "seedlings" it seems a pity that so much valuable land and so much time should be lost, when the remedy is so simple. The plants thus put in are often two feet high, and with several primaries (i.e., crowned, as I found afterwards). Their rootlets are torn and lacerated, and the check they thus receive in transplanting, and in being suddenly taken out from shade and exposed to the fierce rays of a tropical sun, results either in a large percentage being killed or in the plants being two or three years before they produce a maiden crop.

But still as the planters say, many of the plants do grow and when they do they produce some of the best coffee in the world.

In colour, the best Jamaica coffee is darker and bluer than Ceylon coffee, and the beans smaller. Whether the color shows a larger proportion of oil I know not, but the sample appears to be greatly judged and valued according to colour. The sample sent reminds one, in size of the beans, of Mocha coffee, only the beans of the latter are generally of a dark yellow color. Nearly all West Indian and Brazilian coffees are bluish or greenish gray.

The color of the bean must depend, in some measure, on the manner of pulping and drying, but, so far as I have noticed, the processes in Jamaica are much the came as in Ceylon, except that, possibly, here the cherry is allowed to stand longer before it is pulped.

But to return to the question of high prices—why does Jamaica coffee command such high prices? This subject, and especially in connection with Mocha coffee, must have occupied the attention of coffee-planters ever since coffee-planting began, but, so far, it appears not to have received a satisfactory solution. Is it temperature, atmospheric pressure, natural fertility, humidity of soil or air, amount of sunlight and excessive stimulation which produced the perfect elaboration of those subtle principles upon which the aroma and active qualities of coffee depend?

With regard to Mocha and Jamaica coffee, there must evidently be a combination of very favorable conditions for the production of beans possessing such salutary and agreeable qualities; but from the subtlety and delicacy of the laws of vegetable assimilation, I fear it is almost impossible so to analyse and trace these conditions as to produce their parallel in other coffee-producing countries.

Jamaica Blue Mountain® coffee's fine flavour is now attributed to a combination of factors: the soil (shale), altitude, temperature variations and length of growth.

Over the years, several other coffee varieties were planted in Jamaica. Some had limited success and others none at all, and it is the arabica variety that is widely planted all over the island to produce the Blue Mountain, High Mountain Supreme, and Jamaica Prime coffees.

Expansion of cultivation

During the last 20 years, and as far back as 1953, Japanese coffee importers have been buying Jamaica Blue Mountain® coffee. In fact, the demand has outstripped the supply, with buyers paying as much as 15 to 20 times the average price for coffee. It became imperative that the Jamaica Blue Mountain® coffee area be defined. In 1983, an amendment to the Coffee Industry Regulations, 1953 defined the area as:

Starting at Skibo and proceeding in an easterly direction to Swift river; thence east-south easterly to Chelsea; thence east-south easterly to Durhan (Samba Hill); thence south-easterly to Belleview; thence south-easterly along the western slope of the John Crow mountain to Cedar Grove; thence westerly to Font Hill; thence north-westerly to Ramble; thence westerly to Good Hope; thence north-westerly to Dallas; thence north-north-westerly to Industry Village; thence north-north westerly to Maryland;

thence north-westerly to Golden Spring; thence northerly to Brandon Hill; thence north-easterly to Tranquility; thence east-north easterly to Skibo.

It was decided by the government of the day to expand coffee production, particularly of Jamaica Blue Mountain® coffee, by deregulating the industry and issuing licenses to process and market coffee to anyone who produced 10,000 boxes of coffee a year.

Loans were in place from the government of Japan to the government of Jamaica, which disbursed them through the Coffee Board. These loans were swiftly taken up by highly placed and many middle-class persons wishing to go into coffee—mainly Jamaica Blue Mountain®—production. Although loans were available for the expansion of lowland coffee cultivation, few growers were interested, and the funds reverted to Jamaica Blue Mountain® coffee production. This meant that, for the first time since emancipation in 1838, coffee was seen as a good investment by other than peasant farmers.

The loans carried a stipulation that repayment would be in beans, a request made by the Japanese government. To date, however, the payments have been negligible—so negligible that the Coffee Board has been put in an embarrassing position, as they have been unable to repay the Japanese lenders.

Jamaica Blue Mountain® coffee–production entities that existed before the deregulation are Wallenford Factory and Estate Coffee, owned by Wallenford Coffee Company Limited (formerly the Coffee Industry Board Commercial Division), Blue Mountain Coffee Cooperative (Moy Hall factory), Jablum (Mavis Bank factory). In 1992, the deregulated Blue Mountain group entities included Supreme Jamaica Coffee Coop, Premier Coffee Trading Co, Al and Newcastle Blue Mountain Coffee Coop (the last is no longer in operation). By 2003, the estate group included Old Tavern (1997), RSW (Resource, Whitfield Hall, Sherwood Forest), Blue Mountain Coffee Ventures, Greenwich Coffee Company and Dyoll Wataru. The deregulated lowland coffee entities included Jamaica Standard Products, Barron Hall, Salada, Jablum and Coffee Industries of Jamaica.

In 2000, the functions of the Coffee Industry Board were separated into two divisions, commercial and regulatory. The commercial division, would finance restructuring, obtain proper management, improve quality and efficiency and diversify the market. In 2002, sales to non-Japanese markets increased by 150 per cent over the previous year. New markets were opened in China and Spain. The regulatory division was to be involved in the granting of licences to individuals or companies for estate coffee; restructuring of the extension services; creating a database for farmers; controlling the berry borer, which causes loss of some 10 per cent of the crop; protecting the Jamaica Blue Mountain® trademark; and overseeing quality control. This section was also mandated to promote expansion and increased production, from an average of 14 boxes per acre to at least a break-even 42 boxes.

In August 2004, the two divisions of the Board became two separate and distinct legal entities. The Wallenford Coffee Company Limited assumed the functions of the commercial division, with the Board retaining the regulatory functions.

Environmental problems

In the 1980s, the sudden expansion of the coffee industry in the Blue Mountains produced severe ecological effects, from deforestation to landslides and the drying up of some streams. Contamination of the rivers and streams with chemicals from the spraying of the trees is affecting drinking water.

The late Bea Lim wrote to the *Gleaner* newspaper, in 1992:

But there is a downside to the extensive planting of coffee in Jamaica, however. In all the frenzied activity to plant coffee, there is no regulatory board or even meaningful concern in environmental quarters, it appears, when natural forests are being cut down to plant coffee and no supervision of the extensive use of insecticides and herbicides by the coffee farmers to spray coffee and keep down weed. The use of these toxic chemicals are affecting plant and animal life and most importantly, no one is analyzing the pollution caused by the run-offs of these chemicals into the streams and rivers, which are the vital sources of water to thousands of Jamaicans.

... [S]ome years ago, CIDCO (Coffee Industry Development Company) cut down hundreds and hundreds of acres of natural rain forests behind Hardware Gap stretching to the very edge of the Hermitage Dam. They did the same thing at Silver Hill Gap. This devastation is still evident many years later, because sadly enough, not only are these hundreds of acres currently still bereft of all but a few desultory coffee bushes, CIDCO has not farmed coffee successfully on these mountain slopes, but the benefit of Jamaica's water-shed provided by the trees in the natural forest there, which existed for thousands of years, is gone—certainly for our lifetime.

... There have been several reports of the rapid decrease in the population of river mullet and river shrimp in rivers like the Spanish river, which the people who live in the area claim has been caused by the large coffee farmers on the slopes above the Spanish river. This story could be multiplied tenfold, wherever coffee is planted on mountain slopes in Jamaica.

Not all new coffee planters have been so negligent but the get rich quick syndrome cannot pay—as care of the plants and hard work will prove beneficial to those farmers that view their coffee as a long term investment.

A spokesman from the Coffee Industry Board explained that FIDCO, the Forest Industry Development Company, began reaping pine trees planted in the 1960s on the hillsides. These vacated lands were handed over to CIDC (the Coffee Industry Development Company) to facilitate the new expansion in coffee planting—the Claverty Cottage and Shirley Castle expansion—under a programme funded by the Japanese.

Because of the total reaping of pine trees, the hillsides were left bare and though planting of coffee and shade trees commenced, it would take about three years for the coffee plants to start making an impact and 10 years for the shade trees to come to maturity.

Lessons were learnt from the problems encountered in the 1980s and the Board has developed a 'Code of Practice' which should be applied in the growing of coffee, from land clearing, selection of seedlings, pesticide and fertilizing usages.

Keble Munn, of the Mavis Bank Blue Mountain Coffee factory and a former chairman of the Coffee Board, says that in days gone by nobody was concerned with pollution. Today, environmental controls are being put in place to control dumping of the cherry trash in the river and to require that the water used during the processing is recycled and used for irrigation.

Coffee planters are now encouraged to plant the trees in rows, using specific trees, such as caleander or oil nut, for shade. The coffee parchment—the dry shell that is taken off the coffee before being sold—is being used as insulation between boards and made into pellets for fuel for the Mavis Bank factory.

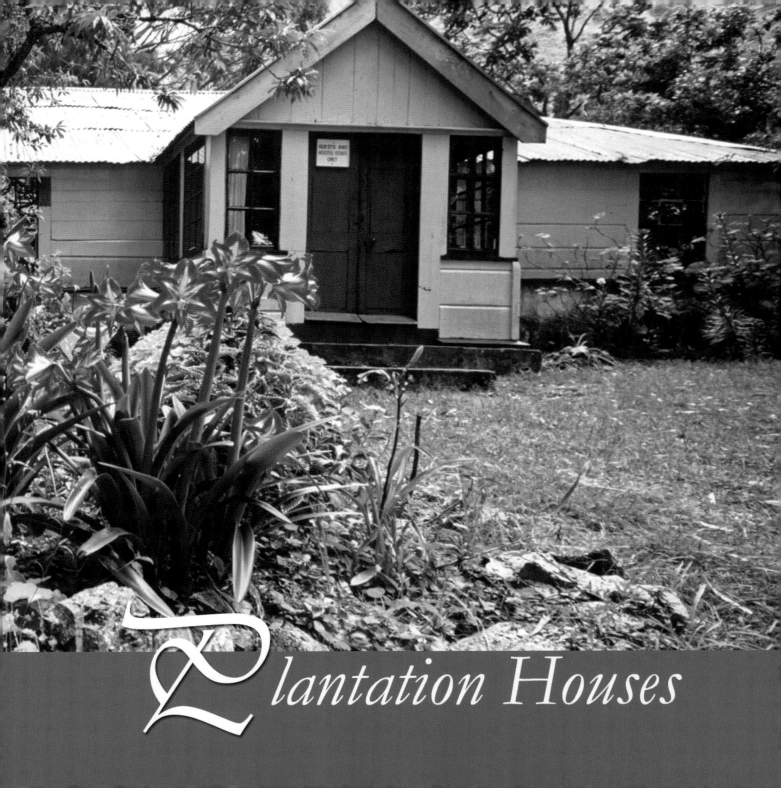

Plantation Houses

The coffee boom in the island lasted a mere 15 years, from 1790 to 1805, but production peaked in 1814, when 34 million pounds of coffee were exported. This huge export was no doubt a result of the enforced storage of coffee between 1806 and 1814, when Napoleon's Continental System kept British goods out of Europe and England was at war with America.

In the 1790s, however, Jamaica stood ready to benefit directly from the revolution in Haiti—then the world's largest producer of coffee, exporting 70 million pounds a year—as coffee supplies to Europe suddenly dried up. Massive coffee planting ensued, helped, to a large extent, by the Haitian coffee planters who fled to Jamaica and who had considerable expertise in this field. One of them was Pierre-Joseph Laborie, a Creole lawyer, whose manual on the growing of coffee, *The Coffee Planter of Saint Domingo* (1798), was to remain the template for the layout, planting and processing of coffee in Jamaica. This model, based on lands in St. Domingue, came under great pressure,

"Jamaica stood ready to

Previous Page: Whitfield Hall

especially in the eastern sections of the Blue Mountains, where the land was rugged and precipitous.

Laborie developed two models of settlement. The first, intended for less steep locations, advocated a tight arrangement of a village with the storage area attached to the main house. To the north of it were sited the gardens and orchards; to the west and adjacent, the drying platforms or barbecues and mill areas; to the east, the stables; and to the south, the Negroes' houses. All these were surrounded by the coffee bushes, provision grounds and woodlands. He advised that, if necessary, the settlement be relocated so as not to be disturbed by travellers.

The second model placed the settlement on top of a steep mountain. The land below, terraced and planted with coffee, fell away from the main house and working areas and the Negroes' houses, which would be reorganised to fit the terrain.

Should a public road pass through the property (as, for example, at Middleton), he recommended that access roads be built between the settlement and fields, although he admitted that 'the nature of the ground seldom permit to adopt that regular method'. Where it was steep, the road would have to 'turn and wind' which was how many of the roads in the Blue Mountains were built.

Although in 1799 there were some 686 coffee plantations, 465 had been abandoned by 1847. Many coffee planters had already gone bankrupt as a result of the Continental System blockade, the British war with America and high duties. Full emancipation of the slaves in 1838 was the *coup de grâce* for large coffee plantations. Many were abandoned or subdivided and sold to the new peasantry, who became the new coffee planters.

efit...the coffee boom lasted 15 years"

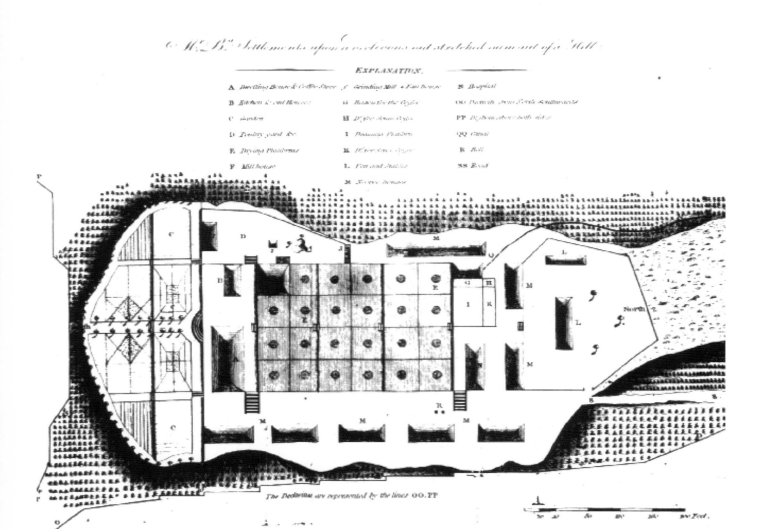

Laborie's ideal layout of a coffee plantation on a steep slope. (Higman)

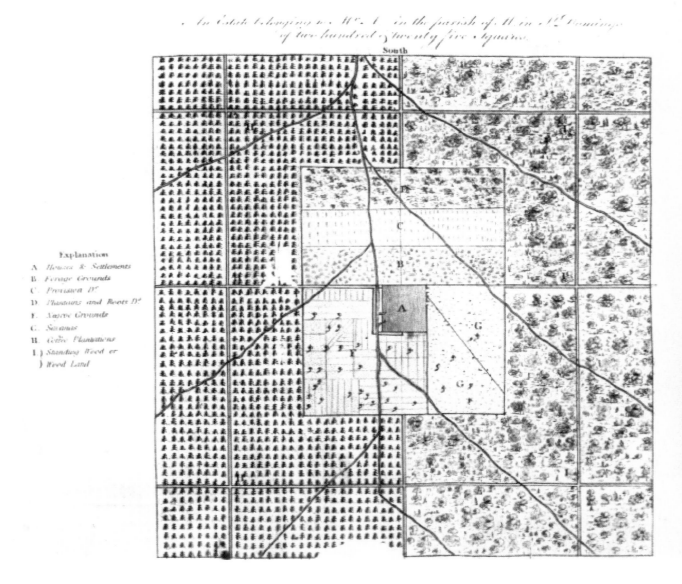

An estate belonging to Mr. A. in parish of Hanover in St. Domingo - 255 squares. (Laborie, 1798)

Luckily, some of the coffee plantation houses have survived. On other plantations, the old houses have been demolished and new houses built on the old sites. Following are a few examples of old coffee estates and houses. Most of the estates had an overseer's house built near to the coffee barbecues, from where, at a glance, he could inspect the processing of the coffee. Very few of the coffee estates had what are known as Great Houses.

Abby Green

The overseers' houses at Abby Green and Whitfield Hall are the only two that were built of wood that have survived the passage of time.

Right: Arntully

Arntully

Arntully is situated in the mountains of St Thomas parish, between 3,000 and 5,500 feet above sea level At the time of emancipation it was owned by William Rae, who also owned the nearby property, Brook Lodge. In 1839, at the time of Rae's death, Arntully consisted of 619 acres, with coffee covering only 86 acres; the rest was in grass, provision grounds, woodland and ruinate. The property next belonged to Charles Lascelles; it comprised 736 acres, with 112 acres in coffee. By 1890, when it was owned by W. Sabonidere (probably French from Haiti), it covered some 924 acres. In 1839 there were 15 coffee fields divided into 5.8 acres each. By 1860 these had increased to 35.

In 1839 no Great House existed. The slave houses were situated in the middle of the coffee north of the works, and the coffee works were towards the south of the property. That year, the area occupied by the slave houses was converted into coffee fields, and the houses were placed further away. By 1860, the former site of the Negro houses had become known as Negro House Flat. A house existed in 1865, however, as on Sunday, October 15, 1865, during the Morant Bay rebellion, 120 soldiers commanded by Colonel Hobbs were stationed at Arntully Great House. They were sent to apprehend Paul Bogle and marched some five miles to Monklands, but Bogle escaped on horseback.

Bellevue–Guava Ridge

The property of Bellevue and the surrounding areas seem to have been settled by French émigrés from Haiti. Many French surnames, such as Duval and Petinaud, have survived, as has the use of words like 'leggings' for legumes and 'gata' for sweet biscuits.

Bellevue is said to have been built by a French émigré called Arboutin, in the 1790s. It was later bought by Sir Alexander Sweethenham, the then governor of Jamaica, who owned it between 1912 and 1931. People in the area remember that it took 16 men five days to transport his grand piano to the house. Both he and his wife apparently were keen gardeners, importing flowers and plants from all over the world for the Bellevue gardens.

Cold Spring

Matthew Wallen came to Jamaica in 1747. He was an Irish naval officer and naturalist who introduced many plants to the mountain area of Jamaica, including the now common watercress, nasturtium dandelion, apple, peach and strawberry; he also grew tea and even a species of bamboo. He married Catherine Phillip, daughter of Colonel Robert Phillip, in 1748. They had four children between 1749 and 1759. Catherine died in 1762. Matthew later married again and with his second wife, Sarah, had two more children. Wallen was a member of the Assembly for the parish of Port Royal.

Wallen owned two coffee properties in the parish of St Georges: Cold Spring, with 300 acres, and Wallenford, a few miles away, to which he gave his name. Wallenford is now owned by the Coffee Board of Jamaica and produces very fine Jamaica Blue Mountain® coffee. William Hickey, in his *Memoirs* (1776), wrote that Cold Spring took its name from 'a remarkably cold and beautifully clear spring that issues from a fissure in the rock, supplying the family with the best water I had ever tasted. To the touch it was like ice itself' (p. 45).

Colonel Wallen died in 1797. Cold Spring was mentioned by John Bigelow in 1850 (p.167–68): 'Cold spring coffee field which is owned in London by a Mr Hamilton and is said to produce the finest coffee that is taken into Liverpool where it commands 140/- per cwt.'

Today, the original house is no longer standing, and the present cottage seems to have been built about 1920. However, the barbecues and the ruins of the pulpery, works and floating ponds are still on the property, which is now much smaller and is owned by Eleanor Jones. The house, set in a beautiful flower garden, is used for weddings, luncheons and stop-over guests.

Charlottenburg

Considered to be the most beautiful of the coffee plantation houses, Charlottenburg represents an island version of English Regency style, built entirely of wood. Perched on top of Tontent Hill, it has a wide view of the city and harbour. In 1781 the owner, Tesser Samuel Kuckahn, was growing peaches, apples and vegetables in the extensive gardens that he had established. He died in 1812, and the property was bought by the Dolmage family, who were most likely of French origin. It then became the property of the Anglican Bishop Spencer, who used it as a retreat from the heat of the city. It was he, no doubt, who established the terraced gardens.

At the end of the nineteenth century, Charlottenburg belonged to the Casserly family and was used as a retreat by the Franciscan order of monks. The property now belongs to the Bitter family, but the beautiful house was recently destroyed by fire.

Chesterfield

Chesterfield is first mentioned in the Accounts Produce for 1794, when the property was owned by the estate of Archibald Thompson, whose widow, Mrs Jane Thompson, had taken over the management of the plantation. By 1818 James Muir was the proprietor; he was followed by Alexander Bizzet in 1838 and Charles and George Barclay in 1854. Coffee production started off modestly: in 1794 the estate produced some 13,242 pounds. Either the property was expanded or larger tracts of the land were placed in coffee production, because in 1829 the reported crop was 145,831 pounds. The last reported crop was mentioned in the *Jamaica Almanac* of 1830.

The slaves were housed near the coffee fields in the parish of St. David, now St. Thomas, and the estate's white staff in the parish of Port Royal (now St. Andrew). The *Jamaica Almanac* reported that 148 persons lived on the plantation in 1818.

The overseer's house is intact, and the remains of a Great House, which was unusual on coffee plantations, can be seen. Only the barbecues are intact; some are terraced into the hillside. Nothing remains of the coffee works, which were probably built of wood.

Clydesdale

This house, built about the 1820s, lies some 12 miles by road from Middleton and is another example of a coffee house built in a deep valley by a river, so the mills could use the water for pulping. It appears that Clydesdale was at one time a part of the Chestervale plantation. In 1800 the owner of Chestervale, Dr Colin McCarty, divided the estate into four pieces. He kept 874 acres, and two pieces became Newport Hill, owned by William Griffiths. The fourth piece, consisting of 329 acres, became Clydesdale, the property of Alexander McCarty.

The architecture suggests French influence in the dormer windows, typical of French houses in the island. The mill and water wheel were situated on the ground floor of the two-storey stone structure, which is still intact. The upper floor was probably used by the overseer or bookkeeper.

The plantation's largest crop was recorded in 1829, when it produced 77,564 pounds of coffee.

Craighton

Close to Middleton is Craighton House, which started out as the residence of the governors of the island. It was built about 1805, and after the military camp was built at Newcastle in the late 1830s, it was frequently occupied.

The eighth Earl of Elgin lived at Craighton between 1842 and 1846. His wife, whose memorial can be seen at the Spanish Town cathedral, died there in June 1843. The earl later became governor general of Canada (1847–54) and of India (1862–63).

In 1873, Craighton became the home of Sir John Peter Grant, governor from 1866 to 1873. Prior to his appointment to Jamaica, he had been the lieutenant governor of Bengal. Some of the institutions he set up have survived to this day.

Coffee has been grown at Craighton for almost 100 years by subsequent owners. Most recently, it was owned by Sir Robert Kirkwood, before it was sold to the Ueshima Coffee Company of Japan in 1983.

Dallas Castle

Not far from Bellevue, near Flamstead, is the property known as Dallas Castle, which was owned by a Dr Dallas during the mid-eighteenth century. There he brought up his numerous children, some of whom were to become prominent citizens in the island. Two of them gained wider fame. One was Robert Charles Dallas, who wrote the *History of the Maroons*. He was well known in English literary circles. His nephew was Lord Byron, whose early poems he helped to publish.

Another son, Alexander Stuart Dallas, left the island for Philadelphia in 1873. There he studied law and entered politics, eventually being appointed Secretary of the Treasury. His son, George Miflin Dallas, was elected vice president in 1848 and gave his name to Dallas, Texas.

Mavis Bank

Situated at 2,500 ft above sea level in the lower levels of the Blue Mountain, Mavis Bank had some 302 acres in 1808. Though considered a small plantation, it shipped 73,339 pounds of coffee to London merchants in 1808.

The works were separated from the milling area, as the pulping mill was supplied with water from a gutter that led to a spring. An overseer's house was located near the works, as is common on coffee plantations. The Negroes' houses stood near the mill and the works. Like many other coffee plantations, soon after emancipation the property was subdivided and sold to 17 purchasers, shown on the plan of 1841 by John M. Smith.

Middleton

The most extensive information on coffee plantations in Jamaica is in the Stowe Collection at the Huntington Library. These papers cover the properties Merrymans Field and Middleton, plantations owned by the Dukes of Buckingham and Chandos. Detailed information on these properties is in chapter 4, 'The Jamaican Coffee Story'.

Priory

This house, at the soldiers' training camp at Newcastle, appears to be the original house. Not much is known about it, but it may have been built by a French émigré from Haiti.

Sherwood Forrest

Thomas Cuming was the owner of Sherwood Forrest in 1801, with 367 acres. William Rae, who owned Arntully in 1821, became the owner of Sherwood Forrest in 1827, and at his death in May 1837, the property was bequeathed to his heirs. When he died, Rae owned Sherwood Forrest, Eccleston, Brook Lodge, River Head and Arntully. The largest coffee crop produced by Sherwood Forrest, 108,293 pounds, was recorded in 1838. Hugh Leslie appears to have been the owner of the property in 1848.

The Sherwood Forrest overseer's house remains standing. Built in two different stages, the basic structure is of made of stone. Unusually, it not only housed the mill works but had rooms above that were occupied by the overseer. It also had a verandah from which the overseer could look down at the barbecues where the coffee beans would be put to dry. The barbecues are set into the hillside, similar to those at Chesterfield

Radnor

Radnor and Springfield plantations were adjoining properties owned by Robert Morgan, an absentee owner from 1808 up to the period of emancipation. Situated some 3,000 to 5,000 feet above sea level in a rugged area of the Blue Mountains, the coffee works were a few miles from the Blue Mountain peak (7,000 feet). Of the 689 acres at Radnor, 236 were in coffee, and it was coffee of superior quality. During the time it was owned by Morgan, Radnor sold

Right: Sherwood

12

MILES
FROM
KGN

151,948 pounds of coffee. There is no record of a house at Radnor at that time, but the overseer, John McGillivay, must have had accommodation there or at Springfield.

Radnor was owned by Sir Anthony Musgrave when he was governor of the island, between 1877 and 1882. After his death in 1889, it was sold to J. Stephens. At this time Radnor occupied some 1,000 acres, of which about 200 were in coffee.

In more recent times, Radnor was owned by a group that included Ainsley Henriques, but it has now been sold to an electrical engineer named Lloyd Dixon.

Whitfield Hall

Whitfield Hall estate, situated in the old parish of St David, was one of the coffee plantations high in the mountains, not far from the Blue Mountain peak. The house, built of wood, has survived, which is rare.

In the early 1800s, the property belonged to Thomas Leigh, who lived there with his wife, Ann, and daughters Sarah and Ann. Leigh died in 1818. Although by 1829 the property was in receivership, the plantation produced its largest crop, 56,673 pounds, in 1827. By the time emancipation was fully effected, parts of the property had been rented to former slaves. The last entry in the Accounts Produce for coffee produced from the estate was in 1847.

Whitfield Hall is owned by John Allgrove. The house is now run as a hostel and is often used as an overnight stop by hikers to the Blue Mountain peak .

TO

UCC

CRAIGHTO

ESTATE

The Japanese Connection

TO
UCC
CRAIGHTON
ESTATE
4 MILES

Japanese involvement in the purchasing of Jamaican coffee began in 1953, when representatives of Japan came to the island to have discussions with the Coffee Industry Board. They were interested in dealing directly with the board and not through the traditional trading companies in England. Ever since, the Japanese have bought almost all of the island's Jamaica Blue Mountain® coffee and other coffees as well. In fact, the demand is greater than the supply.

The government of Japan has provided loans for the expansion of the coffee industry, and so have the Japanese importers of Jamaican coffee. A few of them became involved in joint-venture farms with local businessmen, in an effort to improve production. One of these was the Ueshima Coffee Company.

"the Japanese have bought al

Ueshima Coffee Company

The Ueshima Coffee Company, one of several Japanese companies that buy Jamaican coffee, is considered to be the largest coffee importing company in Japan. Before 1980, Ueshima bought coffee directly from the Coffee Board at a negotiated price. In 1980, the Japanese government, through a bilateral agreement, requested that the company invest in Jamaica not only by buying the coffee but by becoming involved in its production.

It was the dream of UCC's chairman, Tadao Ueshima (now deceased), for the company to have its own coffee plantation. This came about through a government-to-government agreement under which Ueshima established a local company in 1981 and in 1983 bought Craighton, in Irish Town. The company was to acquire two other farms, one at Skibo in Portland and another at Constitution Hill, in joint ventures. However, they terminated the latter two arrangements, keeping only Craighton, mainly as a promotional entity for their sales of Jamaica Blue Mountain® coffee in Japan.

After Hurricane Gilbert did considerable damage to the coffee in 1988, UCC provided a US$5 million loan through the Coffee Board, a part to be used by the board and a part for loans

all of the island's Jamaica Blue Mountain® coffee..."

to the farmers. In addition, the other seven members of the Coffee Association of Japan (including UCC) gave US$1 million each in loans to the Coffee Board for resuscitation of the crop.

Mr Seyama, the then manager, said that it was much easier for the Japanese coffee importers to deal with the Coffee Board, but following deregulation they had to negotiate separately with each licensed exporter of both Jamaica Blue Mountain® and lowland coffees. He emphasised that if customers were expected to pay some 20 times the price of any other coffee, the high quality of Jamaican coffee had to be maintained.

Ueshima Coffee Company sells its coffee—both 100 per cent Jamaica Blue Mountain® and Blue Mountain blends—in its outlets throughout Japan. In 1989 the company established a Kona coffee plantation in Hawaii.

Japanese coffee products

Canned hot and cold coffee drinks, made from blends containing Jamaican coffee, are becoming popular in Japan. But Jamaica Blue Mountain® coffee, because of its rarity and high price, is served only in very exclusive Japanese clubs. Jamaican coffee is also used in many Japanese confections.

Jamaican coffee products

The island can be justly proud of its chief coffee products, the liqueurs made from Jamaica Blue Mountain® coffee, manufactured by Sangsters, Wray and Nephew Ltd and Cottage Industries Ltd. Tia Maria®, the most famous of the coffee liqueurs, had an interesting beginning.

Morris Cargill, the well-known Jamaican journalist and attorney-at-law, tells about the creation of Tia Maria® liqueur in his book *Jamaica Farewell*. During the World War II years, when he was in England, he spent a considerable amount of time in working-class pubs. The men drank large quantities of beer, while the women unenthusiastically preferred sweet drinks like cherry brandy.

Cargill thought of the delicious rum-based liqueurs that his aunt used to make in Jamaica— in particular, a coffee liqueur. It would be a winner, he thought, as caffeine would 'neutralise the depressant effect of the alcohol' and lower the drinker's inhibitions. So, in 1946, he returned to Jamaica to get the recipe from his aunt, who, by that time, remembered neither him nor the liqueur, much less how it was made. Needless to say, he was thoroughly discouraged, but someone told him about Ken Evans, the government pathologist, who, as a hobby, was experimenting with the making of liqueurs.

This was the start of the coffee liqueur. Evans created a recipe that enabled them to produce the liqueur in bulk without variations in quality, using Keble Munn's (a coffee planter, former cup-tester and chairman of the Coffee Industry Board) fine Jamaica Blue Mountain® coffee. Cargill's old friend J.P. MacNulty, who ran a small advertising business in London, designed the label and named the product after Cargill's Aunt Mary.

The coffee was an instant success in English pubs. Later, transcending the class barrier, it became the world's most famous liqueur. Herbert Hart, who Cargill met when Hart was assistant manager of the Palace Amusement Company, in 1940, enlisted in the Second World War and returned to Jamaica after the war. In the early stages of the production of coffee liqueur Hart and Cargill, assisted by Paul Geddes of Desnoes and Geddes Limited with some equipement, formed a company—Estate Industries Limited—to market the coffee liqueur (Tia Maria®). Cargill eventually sold their 50 per cent share in Estate Industries, and the original label was changed from 'Jamaica Liqueur' to 'Coffee Liqueur'.

A coffee jelly is manufactured by Scotts under the Busha Browne label.

Growing & Marketing
Coffee in Jamaica

Gone are the days when coffee seedlings were pulled up from around the trees and planted. The Coffee Industry Board now ensures that only high-quality seedlings, grown in nurseries, are sold to coffee farmers. Two types of seedlings are available for planting: 'barefoot' seedlings (Jamaicans try to find interesting names for the seedlings) and potted seedlings.

The barefoot seedlings are grown in beds until they are ready for transplanting. The advantages of this method are that barefoot seedlings are cheaper to produce and transport, and the root system, which has to be right, can be checked on the spot. There are, however, some disadvantages—both quick and skilful planting and very frequent watering are necessary.

"Jamaica Blue Mountian® c

Potted seedlings have a low mortality rate, are easier to plant, can be kept for a long time in plastic bags, and need less watering. However, they are more expensive both to produce and to transport.

Coffee is traditionally planted during the two main rainy periods of the year, May and October. Fertilizing and organic manuring are also done at these times.

Depending on the topography, either continuous furrows or separate holes, two feet square, are dug to receive the new plants. The holes are filled with topsoil, organic manure and fertiliser, and the rest of the soil is placed in a mound over each hole or furrow. Planting takes place a few weeks later when the ground is soaked through and the earth has subsided. Each hole is opened to allow a new plant to be placed in it. Each plant has to be checked for a sound root system, which consists of a perfect taproot. The holes are then filled in with earth, which is tamped down into a depression for catching water.

Triple stems

The plants are not allowed to grow into straight trees, but are bent over and anchored when they have about nine inches of hard wood. Numerous shoots will result, from which three are selected; the others, as well as the top of the plant, are snipped off.

e is grown at an elevation above 2,500 feet..."

Although arabica will grow to a height of 10 feet, in Jamaica it is pruned when it is four or five feet tall, to enable easy access for picking of the berries and to encourage more foliage and stem growth—and thus more coffee per plant. The plant's first bearing occurs at three years old. Many farmers intercrop with cash crops such as cucumbers, carrots, escallion, red kidney beans and sweet potatoes.

Depending on the area where the coffee is planted, temporary shade might be have to be provided. Banana trees are often used, followed by permanent leguminous plants, such as *Albizzia lebbick* (woman's tongue) and *Inga vera* (locust) when the coffee plants are fully grown.

Pests *and* diseases

The number one enemy of coffee is considered to be the coffee berry borer, which appears to have been present in the island for at least 100 years. There was a severe outbreak of the insects in 1977–78. The borer (*Hypothenemus hampei*) does extensive damage to the coffee bean. It enters through the opening at the bottom of the young bean; the female bores her way to the parchment (endocarp) of the bean, and then, about two months later, starts laying an average of 70 eggs per month. When the larvae hatch, they begin feeding on the bean.

Other pests include the white coffee leaf miner (*Leucoptera coffeealla*), green scale (*Coccus virdis*), black stem borer (*Apate terebrans*), cicada, slugs, nematodes, spider mites, mealy bugs and rats. Rats pluck off the ripe berries and neatly hull and eat the sweet pulp under the skin of the beans. They let the beans fall under the tree. Children are sent to gather these 'rat cut' berries, which are processed for home consumption.

The coffee leaves are also susceptible to various diseases, such as Cercospora leaf spot (*Cercospora coffeicola*), American leaf spot (*Mycena citricolor*), anthracnose (*Colletotrichum coffeanum*) and coffee berry disease (*C. coffeanum* var. *virulans*), a type of anthracnose found at high elevations.

Control

The coffee plant is sprayed with thiodan, to control the infestation of the coffee berry. However, the use of this chemical is being phased out in keeping with international requirements. An innovative trap called a Brocap, developed in El Salvador, has been in use here for about five years. A mixture of ethanol and methanol, which mimics the smell of the young green berries, is placed in the trap to attract the borer. Tiny wasps imported from Central America are also used to control the borer. The plants are periodically sprayed to control the other pests and diseases. Rat baits are set in the fields to control rodents.

The Coffee Industry Board has been actively promoting and advocating the use of a four-pronged integrated disease and pest management system encompassing proper field sanitation practices, the Brocap trap, parasitoids and chemicals as the best approach.

Harvesting

The coffee berries are picked by hand when they are cherry ripe and must be delivered to the pulpery or collected by Coffee Industry Board or cooperative trucks the same day to prevent fermentation.

Jamaica Blue Mountain® coffee is pulped at the Wallenford Factory and at cooperatives and private factories that have been deregulated, such as, Moy Hall in St. Thomas—the Blue Mountain Coffee Cooperative run by the Jamaica Agricultural Society—and Mavis Bank in St. Andrew. Pulperies outside the Blue Mountain area include those at Aenon Town, Clarendon Park and Trout Hall in the parish of Clarendon; Maggotty in St. Elizabeth; and Bog Walk in St. Catherine.

Processing

The coffee delivered to the factories is pulped to remove the outer red skin, then passed to the aquapulper, which washes the sweet pulp off the seed. The wet coffee or parchment coffee[1] is kept in storage tanks filled with water that is changed frequently to prevent fermentation. On some estates, the coffee is only pulped, then it is left in water for eight to twenty-four hours to

remove the sticky substance. However, great care has to be taken that it does not spoil through over-fermentation. Trucks then carry the beans to the finishing and grading factory or to other factories. The coffee is further dried in special driers to a moisture content of about 12 per cent. The dried parchment beans are placed in wooden bins and cured for two months.

Some privately owned estate coffees are processed on the estates themselves.

Hulling and grading

The coffee is stored (cured) for approximately eight weeks after the drying process, then hulling and the final processing commence. Coffee beans are hulled in mechanical hullers, which remove the husk and the silvery inner membrane that surrounds the beans.

After the beans (of both Jamaica Blue Mountain® and lowland coffees) are put on a conveyer belt, which moves them to the graders that remove dirt and other extraneous materials and sort the beans, usually into four sizes. Sizes 3 and 4 of the Jamaica Prime beans are sold to the local market, mainly for the making of soluble (instant) coffee, whereas sizes 1 and 2, the best beans, are delivered on a conveyer belt to electronic colour sorters and hand sorters (usually women) who remove any damaged or discoloured beans.

A batch of 100 bags is called a 'chop', and its identification is determined by cup-testing of samples taken from it, a procedure that is based on international standards.

Jamaican coffees

The types of coffee exported from Jamaica are Jamaica Prime, High Mountain Supreme and Jamaica Blue Mountain®. High Mountain Supreme and Jamaica Prime coffees are grown outside of the defined Blue Mountain coffee area and are referred to as lowland coffee. Each type of coffee is graded to international standards and cup-tested to determine its quality.

In former times, the designation 'Natural' indicated coffee that was dried in its skin. A 'Settler's Wash' was a coffee-processing method that fell between Natural and Washed. These methods of processing have been discontinued.

Jamaica Blue Mountain® coffee

Jamaica Blue Mountain® coffee is grown at an elevation from 500 feet (152.4 m) to about 5000 feet (1,524 m) above sea level in a defined area of the Blue Mountains. This very fine coffee is processed, sorted, cup-tested and graded in several categories.

Grade 1 is of bold appearance and fits on screen 17 or 18 of the international accepted standard. It is blue/green to greenish in colour and has less than three per cent of minor defects and moisture content of 10 to 12.5 per cent. It has a sweet, lovely fragrance and lovely lingering aftertaste, a mellow, sweet taste, moderate acidity and fairly good body. Grades 2 and 3 have all the attributes of Grade 1 but the beans are smaller.

The peaberry, is a small, rounded bean resembling a pea, which comprises about five per cent of the coffee beans produced. It is lighter in body and has higher acidity, with the sweetest taste of all.

Triage is the combination of 'seconds' from grades 1, 2 and 3; it has a less pronounced bouquet than the other grades.

High Mountain Supreme coffee

This coffee is grown in selected high-elevation areas outside of the defined Jamaica Blue Mountain® coffee area. There are two gradings of this coffee. Size 1 beans are bold, fitting international screen 17 or 18, with good bluish-green to greenish colour. Cup-tasting shows good acidity, fairly good body, a pleasant aroma and clean taste. The peaberry has a good aroma, lighter body and better acidity than the flat bean High Mountain Supreme coffee and a sweeter taste.

Prime Jamaica Washed coffee

Jamaica Prime coffee which made up the bulk of Jamaican coffees (up to the mid 1990s) is grown at lower elevations. Jamaica Blue Mountain® coffee production currently outstrips the non-Blue Mountain coffee production. The ratio is now about 5:1 in favour of Jamaica Blue Mountain®.

The Jamaica Prime Coffee, which makes up the bulk of Jamaican coffees, (up to the mid 1990s) has uniform bold beans, almost free from defects and the roast is good. The beans are bluish-green to greenish in colour and fit international screens 17 and 18 (the screens are 17/64 and 18/64 of inches in cross section). The cup quality is particularly soft, with a fair good body, medium acidity and no off flavours. Size 2 is smaller than size 1 but has the same cup-testing results. The peaberry consists of small, roundish beans of good appearance, with a good aroma, fairly good body and acidity and good aftertaste. Other lower grades and size 3 and fines (broken beans) are sold locally.

Jamaica Prime and High Mountain Supreme coffees are exported in bags of 60 kg and wooden barrels of 70 kg net weight respectively. Jamaica Blue Mountain® coffee is also exported in special barrels of 70 kg net weight

Marketing of coffee

The Jamaican coffee crop is tiny compared to those of the large coffee-producing countries. However, the coffee is of the best quality.

Local demand for coffee has increased tremendously over the years. Only about 30 per cent of the coffee grown is consumed locally. Some (not Jamaica Blue Mountain®) coffee is used in the manufacture of instant coffee, some of which is exported. (Liqueurs are usually made from Jamaica Blue Mountain® coffee). Of the 70 per cent that is exported, almost 85 per cent goes to Japan; the rest is sent to Europe and North America. Before the Coffee Industry Board was established in the 1950s, when it became the sole distributor of coffee in the island, individual farmers or agents used to sell coffee on consignment directly to agents in different countries, where the price was determined. This practice continued after the Board was established, but soon afterwards Keble Munn, the then chairman of the board, having read that a crop of grain could be sold on the world market in advance at a set price, decided to try his luck. In fact, he offered ten tons of Jamaica Blue Mountain® coffee for future shipment to the Japanese, and they gave him a very good price. This was the first contract received by the board to supply a fixed amount of coffee at a guaranteed price. This shift in pricing policy allowed farmers to plan ahead, knowing that they would get a set amount of money for their crop.

The Japanese have been buying Jamaica Blue® Mountain coffee since the 1950s. When the Board was involved in commercial activities, it usually negotiated the price with the Japanese. Each year the Japanese buyers and the Board agreed on a price that was satisfactory to the Board.

In 1983, the government deregulated the coffee industry by allowing farmers who produce over 10,000 boxes or 20,000 bushels of coffee to export their own coffee. However, the Board still undertakes rigid quality control for all coffees.

Although some most of the Jamaica Blue Mountain® coffee is sold to the seven Japanese coffee importers, the amount is still negligible. And instead of trading with just the Coffee Board, as they were accustomed to doing in the past, the Japanese now have to negotiate with the various deregulated cooperatives coffee dealers. The Japanese, however, are apparently concerned only with the quality of the Jamaica Blue Mountain® coffee, for which they are paying a premium price. Most of the Jamaica Prime and High Mountain Supreme coffees are also exported to Japan.

---

1. • Wet coffee is coffee that has just been pulped and is still wet. Parchment coffee is coffee that has been pulped and dried where the moisture content is reduced to 12 per cent. At this stage it is called, dried parchment. It is then left to cure in bins for about two months, then hulled, that is, to remove the silver skin or membrane. The coffee beans are green in colour. At the next stage they are sorted into sizes.

The Jamaican Cup-Tester

Each batch of coffee is physically assessed and cup-tested by the Coffee Industry Board's Quality Assurance Department. Roasted samples of various batches of coffee are placed on a revolving table. An amount of 7.5 grams of roasted coffee is placed in each of the three cups used per sample. Boiling water is poured onto the ground coffee in each cup. The coffee is allowed to steep for about two minutes then the contents in the cup are stirred and the aroma is observed. The smell of the ground coffee is the first indication of the type of coffee.

The tester sits directly in front of the cup on the table and observes the aroma. He or she starts by breaking up, with a spoon, the crust that has formed at the top of the coffee, further releasing its aromas. The next step is to slurp a spoonful of the brew into the mouth, swirl it around and then spit it out. By this time, the cup-tester will be able to, not only identify the coffee, but determine its aroma, body, acidity and any foreign odours that it might have picked up.

'It takes years of training t

The expert tester looks first for faults, then for desirable attributes—body, sweetness and acidity. It takes years of training to acquire the sharpened sense of taste and smell that a cup-tester must have to be able to distinguish and identify many different coffees.

Keble Munn

The Coffee Industry Board's first cup-tester was its chairman, Keble Munn. His family's connection with coffee growing goes back to 1885, when his great-grandfather settled at Strawberry Hill in the Blue Mountains. The earliest coffee-related picture of him was taken when he was three years old, standing on a coffee barbecue at Strawberry Hill estate, surrounded by parchment coffee. As a young boy, during school holidays, he used to visit the family's Mavis Bank factory and his uncle Victor Munn's Moy Hall factory.

His family built the Mavis Bank factory for drying the coffee that was produced at Strawberry Hill (Westphalia), where the clouds that constantly hovered gave little time for the coffee to dry. A 25-acre piece of land, then costing £25, was chosen at Mavis Bank, which was lower down the mountain, deep in the valley, on slopes, and faced east and west, for maximum sunshine.

Keble Munn

quire the sharpened sense of taste and smell.

Mr Munn himself was actively involved in coffee growing since 1945, when he returned home from the war. The old factory was pulled down and replaced by a modern one, which has been expanded over the years, and newer machinery and equipment have been installed. Now 140,000 boxes of cherry coffee or approximately 1.4 million pounds (635,036 kilos) of green beans can be processed in each crop.

Keble Munn was one of the deregulated coffee farmers allowed to export coffee. He marketed green beans as Mavis Bank Blue Mountain coffee and roasted coffee as Jablum coffee (the latter is a blend of Jamaican coffees, containing 20 per cent Blue Mountain). He used to say, 'Cup-testing is really a human response—you are looking for acidity [and] flavours, good or bad—and the big thing to remember is that coffee takes up the smell of anything around it.'

David Evans

David Evans is Jamaica's most famous cup-tester, a man whose sensitive nose and tongue can identify almost any coffee in the world. After spending most of his working years at the Coffee Industry Board, he is now retired and does only consulting work. This takes him abroad often, as his expertise is much sought after.

Mr Evans, like Keble Munn, was exposed to coffee growing from a tender age. His grandparents had a 300-acre farm in the parish of Clarendon, outside of the Blue Mountain coffee area, where they grew several crops, including coffee. He, like Keble, spent his childhood summers on the coffee farm. There he watched the workers using the old methods of curing coffee, pulping and washing it in their own hand mill and spreading it to dry in the sun.

He started his working life at various private enterprises and also worked as an auditor with his uncle. In 1951 he worked at the old Agricultural Marketing Corporation, then was transferred to the coffee and cocoa clearing house to do auditing. The manager, Mr Aquart, often sent him to test coffee and cocoa (cacao) beans brought in by merchants.

In 1955, Mr Evans joined the Coffee Board Industry as a cashier, then moved on to become processing cashier. After three years he started learning cup-testing. In 1958 he became pulpery manager in the countryside, where he served for 18 years, following which he was promoted to senior manager of all factories. In the mid-1970s he was brought back to Kingston as processing works and quality control manager. At this point he had been doing cup-testing for 20 years. He was sent to London on a three-month course to finish his cup-testing requirements. The manager of the company where he was sent for training was bewildered by his presence, as Evans already knew everything there was to know about coffee testing.

In 1987 he retired but was brought back, on a contract basis, as quality control manager and continued in that capacity until May 1992. Although he has again retired, Mr Evans continues to be closely involved in the coffee industry, where his expertise is sought not only by many export farmers and the Coffee Industry Board itself but also by other coffee-growing countries.

David Evans

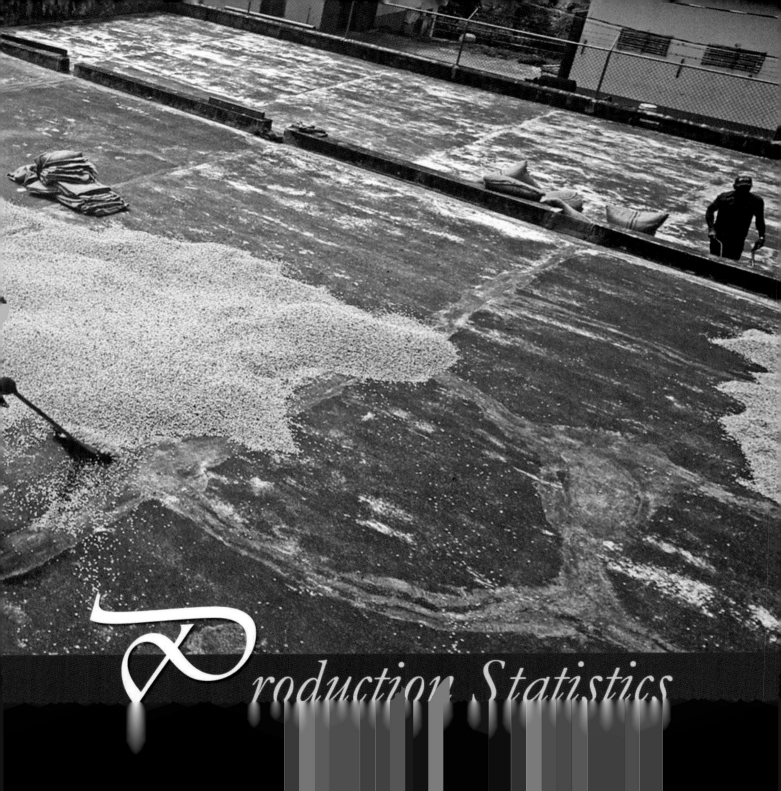

Production Statistics

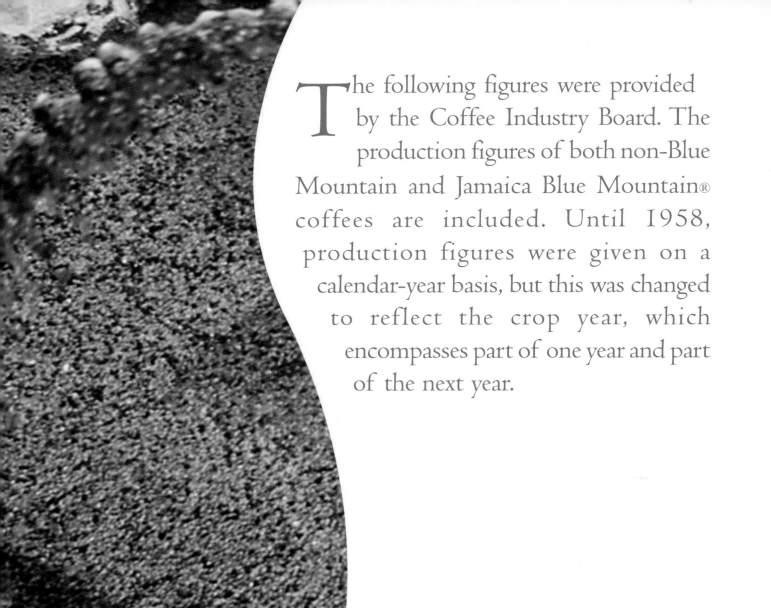

The following figures were provided by the Coffee Industry Board. The production figures of both non-Blue Mountain and Jamaica Blue Mountain® coffees are included. Until 1958, production figures were given on a calendar-year basis, but this was changed to reflect the crop year, which encompasses part of one year and part of the next year.

"In 1972 Jamaica Blue Mounta

Coffee Industry Board's Jamaica Blue Mountain® Coffee Export Figures

Year	Pounds
1953	238,782
1954	533,815
1955	239,805
1956	472,783
1957	222,682
1958/59	241,512
1959/60	191,643
1960/61	134,989
1961/62	244,779
1962/63	192,292
1963/64	205,204
1964/65	137,074
1965/66	150,690
1966/67	123,218

processing factories... were allowed to export their own coffee"

1967/68	83,723
1968/69	112,662
1969/70	N/A
1970/71	277,964
1974/75	683,573

In 1972 the Jamaica Blue Mountain® processing factories Moy Hall and Silver Hill (cooperatives) and Mavis Bank (Jablum) were allowed to export their own coffee. Old Tavern obtained their licences in 1997. Estate licences have also other estates that meet the Coffee Industry Board's specifications. The following figures show the total Jamaica Blue Mountain® coffee production based on the number of boxes of coffee delivered to the Jamaica Blue Mountain® coffee factories Wallenford, Moy Hall, Silver Hill and Mavis Bank since 1980. Each box produces approximately ten pounds of green beans.

1980/81	39,017
1981/82	40,416
1982/83	78,486
1983/84	52,774
1984/85	56,218
1985/86	87,800
1986/87	121,310

1987/88	126,374
1988/89	92,451
1989/90	104,553
1990/91	165,650
1991/92	206,300
1992/93	232,772
1993/94	205,000
1994/95	306,807
1995/96	339,398
1996/97	446,947
1997/98	376,155
1998/99	317,843
1999/00	469,620
2000/01	312,403
2001/02	477,575
2002/03	364,356
2003/04	529,704
2004/05	236,405
2005/06	382,421

Coffee Roasting &
Equipment

The best coffee I have ever roasted was done in a handmade roaster constructed out of a metal cylinder and a coat hanger. It made perfectly roasted coffee, but I had to turn it by hand, bent over a hot stove, for 20 minutes. My electric roaster will do a fair job, but the roast is uneven. The smell of roasting Jamaica Blue Mountain® coffee at the stage where it smokes and crackles usually devastates my neighbours' senses.

In the hilly and mountainous coffee-growing areas of the island, the people used to (and still) roast or 'parch' their coffee in an iron pot or pan placed over a wood, charcoal or gas fire.

The roast of your coffee will depend on the type you buy—the type you wish to make. For example, French and Italian coffees are made from very dark-roasted beans. At the other extreme, a very good coffee such as Jamaica Blue Mountain® should never be darker than a medium roast, as its fine flavour would be destroyed.

"One need not have e.

The brewing of coffee around the world

The brewing of coffee need not be a laborious and difficult task. It is true that, as in cooking, certain rules have to be followed; otherwise, what could have been a divine cup of coffee might well become an indifferent one. There are many ways of making coffee, depending on the type of coffee itself and the culture in which it is made.

One need not have expensive implements to brew good coffee; however, many have been invented for the purpose. The one you choose to buy should depend on the type of coffee you like to drink.

Making a perfect cup

Irrespective of the type of equipment to be used, be sure to do the following.

· Grind the freshly roasted beans just before making the coffee.

· Make sure the brewing equipment is free of all odours and residues, such as detergent.

· Always rinse the equipment thoroughly before making the coffee.

· Use cold water, if possible, spring water.

· For each cup, use two level tablespoons of ground coffee to about 6 ounces (170 ml) of water.

· Brew in very hot water that has been boiled and taken from the fire for a minute or two.

nsive implements to brew good coffee..."

Some do's and don'ts

· Never boil coffee—this will destroy the delicate flavours and leave you with a bitter, tasteless brew.
· Never reheat coffee, place it on a warmer to maintain temperature.
· Avoid using percolators.
· Use coffeepots made of stainless steel, tinned copper or silver.

Coffee-making methods and equipment

Many types of coffee-makers have been invented, from the simple cheesecloth bag to sophisticated espresso machines. Following are some of the methods of making coffee.

Infusion

Infusion is perhaps the simplest method of preparing excellent coffee. This way of brewing coffee has long been the norm in coffee-growing countries. A drawstring cloth bag is filled with the desired amount of coffee, hot water is poured over it and it is left to steep for a few minutes.

Open pot

In this method, the desired amount of coffee is placed in a container. Hot water is poured over it and stirred. The mixture is then left for a few minutes so the grounds will sink to the bottom before the coffee is served. This method is similar to the one used by the cup-tester.

Drip pot

A drip pot can have either two or three parts. The latter type, known as the French drip, is said to have been invented at the beginning of the nineteenth century by the Archbishop of Paris, Jean de Belloy, who called it a *percolateur*. Its three parts are a bottom section to receive the brewed coffee; the middle, a sieve containing the coffee; and an upper section into which the hot water is poured. The hot water trickles down through the coffee, and the brew is collected in the bottom container.

The two-part drip pot also has a base to collect the coffee. Over it fits a receptacle constructed with a sieve at its bottom. Coffee is put in the top section and hot water is poured over it, similar to the filter method.

Filter

The familiar cone-shaped paper coffee filter was an instant success when it came on the market, as it provided a simple way of making good coffee with easier disposal of the grounds. The method is similar to the drip method. A funnel-like receptacle is fitted with the paper filter, coffee is placed inside and hot water is poured over it, to be collected in the container below.

Ibrik or kanaka

Coffee made in the ibrik or kanaka, a receptacle with a wide base, a narrow top and a long handle, is known as Turkish coffee. Coffee is brewed this way throughout the Middle East. It is not known in what country this method was invented, but experts suggest that it was Egypt. Why the coffee became known as 'Turkish' is not clear.

Turkish coffee is thick and muddy in appearance and must have a 'head', or foam, when poured into the cup. It is made from finely pulverised coffee, ground in a special grinder. The coffee is placed in the ibrik and water is poured over it. The brew is then brought to the boil and poured into tiny cups.

At first it was drunk black, but over time sugar and condiments such as cinnamon, cardamom, cloves, nutmeg and even ambergris—said to be an aphrodisiac—were added.

Francis Thurber, in his book *Coffee—From Plantation to Cup* (1842), noted:

In numerous coffee-houses of the Moslem capital [Constantinople] when a person calls for coffee it is specially made for him. Every coffee-house has a number of long handled little brass pots made to hold 1, 2 or more cups as the case may be. They are smaller at the top than at the bottom and are fitted with a little grooved spout, but have no cover. When a cup of coffee is wanted, the requisite amount of finely ground powdered coffee is measured into one of these little coffee pots, water enough to fill the pot is poured in and it is then set upon live coals, it heats up to just the boiling point. It is then, without straining or otherwise settling the grounds, poured out into a tiny cup, and this is Turkish coffee. As may be supposed it is thick, muddy, and the lower half of the cup composed of grounds, but the flavour is good, and I noticed that most Turks swallowed the grounds with the same relish that they showed for the thinner-part of the beverage. Turks never use milk, an abomination.

French press

This coffee-maker appears to have been developed in Italy and became popular in France. It consists of a cylindrical pot with a handle, in which the coffee is placed. Hot water is poured in and left to steep for a few minutes; then a plunger with a fine mesh is inserted and pushed to the bottom. The grounds are pressed down to the bottom of the pot, and the coffee is poured off. The French press method produces a heavy, dense brew with some sedimentation, which may not be to everyone's liking. It has to be drunk immediately or decanted into a thermal container, as it cannot be reheated.

Neapolitan flip-drip

This filter pot was developed in France and later adopted by the Italians as the Neapolitan *macchinetta del caffè*. Basically, it is a double reversible drip pot. Water is placed in the bottom half, and coffee is put in a two-sided strainer at the top of this half of the pot. The other vessel is attached on top. The bottom part, containing the water, is placed on the fire, and when the water begins to boil, the entire container is flipped over, and the water passes through the coffee and is collected in what is now the bottom half of the pot. The coffee grind should not be too fine.

Pumping percolator

This is the least desirable method of making coffee, as it kills the flavour. Water is placed in the pot, and the coffee is put in a perforated basket on a hollow metal stem. The pot is covered and put on the fire, and the stem pumps the boiling water up from the bottom to circulate through the coffee, which is essentially boiled until the desired extraction takes place.

Cona vacuum

The glass balloon, or Cona vacuum, was invented by Robert Napier, a Scottish marine engineer, in 1840. It makes excellent coffee in an attractive manner. It is much used and appreciated in societies that like serving food and drinks in a ceremonial style. The Cona vacuum consists of two glass balloons or bowls. Cold water is placed in the lower bowl and in the upper glass bowl, which is fitted with a funnel in which medium-fine coffee is placed. Both balloons are screwed together and placed over heat. Upon boiling, the water rises in the funnel and spills onto the coffee. When all the water evaporates from the bottom balloon, it is removed from the heat. The vacuum created will draw the brewed coffee back through the funnel into the bottom balloon.

143

Espresso

Espresso, probably the most popular European coffee, results when hot water under pressure

is forced through coffee. The method and machine were developed basically for cafés. This is a superior method, because coffee is made for each individual cup in a few minutes, and the action is so fast that only the aroma and flavour are extracted, leaving behind some of the chemicals that can alter the taste. The brew is made from very dark-roasted coffee, and the result is a heavy-bodied liquid loved by the Italians and French.

There are many types of home espresso machines on the market, but few can truly imitate the café-style espresso coffee produced by the larger, more efficient machines.

Mocha espresso pot

The mocha espresso pot is probably the most useful and least expensive of the espresso-type equipment. It works on the same steam-pressure principle as the larger machines. The top section of the pot consists of a metal container with a fine strainer at the bottom and a funnel in the middle. Water is placed in the bottom section of the pot and coffee in the top section, which is screwed on tightly to the lower half. When the water boils in the lower half, the steam is forced up through the funnel into the top half, collects around the coffee and then is strained as it passes back into the bottom section. This pot makes very good coffee and is ideal for home brewing. The best pots are made in Italy of stainless steel.

Instant coffee

Fine coffees are never made into instant, or soluble, coffees. Instant coffees are usually made from robusta or other low-grade coffees.

Coffee Recipes

Hot Coffee Drinks

Café Noir

1 cup, (3 ozs 80g) ground coffee
4 cups, (1½ pints, 1 liter) boiling water

1. Place the coffee in the strainer of a drip pot.
2. Pour hot water over it, little by little. Makes four cups.

SERVES 4

Café au Lait

In Europe, especially in France, the traditional breakfast is café au lait served in large bowls, into which buttered baguette, brioche or croissant is dipped before eating. In New Orleans, where the French influence still endures, café au lait and beignets make up the traditional breakfast fare. These are still served in the cafés of the French Quarter, where chicory is added to the coffee.

For regular French café au lait you need:

hot coffee
hot milk
sugar to taste

Mix equal quantities of hot coffee and hot milk. Sweeten to taste.

New Orleans Café au Lait

3 tablespoons sugar
2 cups (¾ pint, 500 ml) hot milk
2 cups (¾ pint, 500 ml) hot coffee made from a dark-roasted coffee with chicory

1. Place the sugar in a heavy pan and set over heat.
2. Let it dissolve and turn caramel-coloured.
3. Remove from heat and carefully add the hot milk; stir and add the coffee.

ENOUGH FOR 4

Left: Café Noir

Café Jamaica

This recipe is from the villages and countryside near to the coffee-growing areas.

coconut milk or cream*
hot strong coffee
sugar to taste

To each cup of coffee add coconut milk to your taste, and sweeten if desired.

Coconut milk or cream is made by grating fresh coconut (or chopping fine in a blender), adding some water to it and mixing thoroughly. The milk is then squeezed through muslin or a sieve.

Hawaiian Coffee

1. Equal quantities of grated coconut and hot milk are left to infuse on low heat, then passed through a sieve.
2. Freshly made coffee is added to the milk.
3. The coconut bran that remains is grilled and sprinkled on the hot coffee.

Right: Café Jamaica

150

Cappuccino

1. This coffee requires equal parts of espresso coffee and frothed steamed milk.
2. The milk is frothed from the steam nozzle on the espresso machine.
3. Cappuccino is difficult to make without a steam nozzle.
4. Cappuccino can be sprinkled with cinnamon, fresh grated nutmeg or grated chocolate.

Spiced Coffee

Spiced coffee drinks have been enjoyed by the peoples of the Middle East for centuries. When coffee drinking became a part of life in Europe, cognac and other eau-de-vie liqueurs and other flavourings were added to the coffee, with or without spices. In many instances cream was added.

4 cups (1½ pint, 1 liter) water
½ cup (3 ozs, 88 g) dark brown sugar
2-inch piece cinnamon stick 3 cloves
1 cup (3ozs, 80g) dark-roasted ground coffee

1. In a saucepan heat the water, sugar, cinnamon and cloves. Stir until sugar has dissolved, then bring to a boil.

2. Remove from the heat and stir in the coffee. Allow to draw and settle.
3. Strain and reheat but do not boil.
SERVES 4

Viennese Coffee or Café Borgia

Chocolate, coffee and cream are blended to make this distinctive drink.

1 oz (25g) chocolate
sugar to taste
1 tbsp cream
1 cup (8 fl oz, 250 ml) hot coffee
whipped cream
sprinkling of cinnamon, cocoa or nutmeg

1. Melt the chocolate in a saucepan.
2. Add the sugar and 1 tablespoon cream.
3. Mix and add 1 cup of hot coffee.
4. Serve with whipped cream on top, sprinkled with cinnamon, cocoa or nutmeg.
SERVES 1

152

Coffee Extracts and Liqueurs

In the Caribbean, coffee extracts have traditionally been made and kept on hand to flavour milk, custards or whatever else might need a little coffee flavouring. This recipe is from Haiti.

Coffee Liqueur

10 cups (4 pints, 2.5 liters) water
3 cups (1¼ lb, 525g) sugar
½ lb (250g) freshly roasted and ground
Jamaica Blue Mountain® coffee
1 qt (1½ pint, 1 liter) overproof rum
Makes approximately 2 quarts or 2 liters of
liqueur.

1. Place sugar and water in a saucepan and stir over medium heat until the sugar has dissolved.
2. Boil until the mixture thickens into a syrup. Remove from heat and cool.
3. Place the freshly roasted Blue Mountain coffee in a large bowl and pour the rum over it.
4. Cover with plastic film and leave for two to three days.
5. Pour through a sieve, then through filter paper. To the strained coffee-rum mixture, add syrup to bring the taste to the preferred sweetness.
6. Bottle and leave to age for at least one month.

Coffee Extract

½ lb (250g) freshly roasted and ground
coffee
2 cups (¾ pint, 500ml) boiling water

1. Place the coffee in a drip coffee container, preferably one with a filter, and pour the hot water over it a little at a time.
2. At the beginning, the coffee will begin to expand, but continue to pour small quantities of the water over it until all of the water is used up. Let cool.
3. When extract is completely cooled, pour it into a bottle and screw top on tightly.

After-Dinner Coffee Drinks

Café Brulot

grated zest of 1 orange
grated zest of 1 lime or lemon
3-inch piece cinnamon stick
1 tsp coriander seeds
4 cloves
sugar to taste
½ cup (4 fl oz 125 ml) Grand Marnier® or
Sangsters Wild Orange® liqueur
4 cups (1½ pint, 1 liter) strong hot coffee

1. In a mortar pound together the orange and lemon zest with the cinnamon, coriander and cloves.
2. Place the spices in a bowl.
3. Place bowl in hot water, add the liqueur and ignite.
4. Stir, and when the flames die down add the coffee.
5. Ladle into demitasses and serve at once.

ENOUGH FOR 4

Café Cacao

Cocoa is usually grown in coffee-producing countries. The blend of these two beverages makes a delicious drink. In this recipe, crème de cacao is added to the coffee.

For 1 cup (8fl oz, 250ml) of hot coffee, add 1–2 tablespoons of crème de cacao. Stir and top with cream.

ENOUGH FOR 1

Coffee Cointreau

Add 2 tablespoons of Cointreau® and a little grated lime or lemon peel to each cup of hot coffee.

SERVES 1

Café Royale

Add 2 tablespoons of cognac to each cup of hot, strong, sweetened coffee.

SERVES 1

Left: Jamaica Coffee Rum Grog

Café Gloria

1. To each cup of hot coffee, add sugar to taste.
2. 2 tablespoons cognac
3. A drop or two of vanilla.
4. Stir and serve.

SERVES 1

Coffee Spanish Main

This lovely coffee drink, made from Jamaica Blue Mountain® coffee, was created at the Sheraton-Kingston Hotel (now the Hilton Hotel).

6 fl oz (175ml) Jamaican rum
6 tbsp, sugar
grated rind of 1 orange
¼ tsp grated nutmeg
1 cinnamon stick
6 cups (2 ½ pints, 1.5 liter) hot coffee

ENOUGH FOR 7-8

Place all the ingredients, except the coffee, in the rum and steep for five minutes. Strain and add the coffee to the rum mixture. Serve immediately.

Gaelic or Irish Coffee

2 tsp sugar
3 tbsp Irish whiskey
2 cups (¾ pint, 500ml) strong hot coffee
double cream

1. Mix the sugar, whiskey, and coffee together in a warmed wineglass.
2. Pour cream over the top and do not stir. Serve at once.

ENOUGH FOR 1

Jamaica Coffee Rum Grog

2 oz (50 ml) Jamaica rum
a strip of orange peel
a strip of lime or lemon peel
1 cinnamon stick
4 cloves
1 ½ cups (12 fl oz, 350 ml) hot coffee
2 tsp brown sugar
cream (optional)

Put all the ingredients, except the cream, in a saucepan. Heat gently but do not boil. Strain into two cups and top with cream if desired.

Café Calypso

2 oz (50ml) coffee liqueur
1 oz (25ml) Jamaican rum
2 cups (¾ pint, 500 ml) hot coffee
whipped cream

Mix the liqueur, rum and hot coffee together.
Pour into cups and top with whipped cream.
ENOUGH FOR 2

Cold Coffee Drinks

Spiced Iced Coffee

2 cups (¾ pint, 500 ml) hot coffee
1 cinnamon stick
10 pimento (allspice) berries
strip of orange rind
1 cup ice cream
ice

1. Pour the hot coffee over the cinnamon, pimento berries and orange rind.
2. Leave to steep until it cools to room temperature.
3. When it is cool, strain mixture into a blender and add ice and ice cream.
4. Blend until frothy. Serve immediately.

ENOUGH FOR 2

Jamaica Iced Coffee

Ice cubes
1 cup strong coffee, chilled
½ cup (4 oz, 125ml) coconut milk
sugar to taste
grated nutmeg

1. Place all ingredients in blender.
2. Blend and serve immediately.

SERVES 1

Café Mazagran

This drink was named after a fortress in Algeria by French Foreign Legionnaires.

chilled, sweetened strong coffee
sparkling water or club soda

Mix and pour over ice.

Left: Coffee Caribbean

Honey Iced Coffee

2 cups (¾ pint, 500ml) chilled coffee
honey

Mix coffee and honey together. Pour over
ice and serve.

ENOUGH FOR 2

Pineapple Coffee

1 cup (6 oz, 175g) coffee ice cream
1 cup (8 fl oz, 250 ml) chilled strong coffee
1 cup (8 fl oz, 250 ml) chilled pineapple
juice

Put all the ingredients in a blender with ice
and blend. Pour into glasses and serve
immediately.

ENOUGH FOR 2

Café Frappé

2 cups (¾ pint, 50ml) strong coffee
1 cup (6 oz, 175g) ice cream
sugar to taste

Place all ingredients in a blender with ice
and blend until frothy. Serve immediately.

ENOUGH FOR 2

Coffee Eggnog

2 cups (1 lb 500g) sugar
5 cups (2 pints, 1.25 liters) boiling water
2 cups (7 oz, 900g) ground coffee
12 eggs
8 cups (3 pints, 2 liters) milk
grated nutmeg

1. In a saucepan, boil the water. Add the sugar and stir until it dissolves.
2. Bring mixture to the boil again. Remove from heat and add the ground coffee.
3. Leave to infuse about 20 minutes. Strain the coffee through muslin and set aside.
4. Beat the eggs until fluffy; add the coffee, milk and grated nutmeg.
5. Pour into a punch bowl and ladle into cups filled with crushed ice.
6. Rum can be added if desired.

MAKES APPROXIMATELY 5 PINTS (3 LITERS)

Café Alexandre

Crushed ice
1 cup (8 fl oz, 250 ml) strong coffee, chilled
and sweetened
1 tbsp brandy
1 tbsp crème de cacao
2 tablespoons whipping cream

In a cocktail shaker, blend crushed ice with
other ingredients. Serve immediately. Makes
one serving.

SERVES 1

Coffee Caribbean

2 cups (¾ pint, 500ml) chilled coffee
1 cup (6 ozs, 175g) coffee or vanilla ice
cream
4 tbsp dark rum
sugar to taste

Pour all the ingredients into a blender and
blend quickly. Serve at once, sprinkled with
nutmeg.

SERVES 2

Café Tropicana

1 cup (8 fl oz, 250 ml) chilled strong coffee
1 tbsp rum
sugar to taste
sparkling water or club soda

Combine the coffee, rum and sugar. Pour
over ice in a tall glass. Add soda.

SERVES 1

Cognac Mocha

A divine drink!

1 cup (8 oz, 250 ml) chilled coffee
1 cup (8 oz, 250 ml) brewed chocolate
1 cup (8 oz, 250 ml) milk
1 cup (8 oz, 250 ml) cognac
sugar to taste

Mix all the ingredients and pour over ice.
Serve immediately.

SERVES 4

162

Tia Maria® Liqueur Recipes

The following recipes were developed by Tia Maria®, manufacturers of the liqueur.

Black Maria

2 parts Tia Maria®
4 Parts Coffee
I Part Rum
I part sugar syrup

Jamaica Wonder

I part Tia Maria®
I part dark rum
I part lime juice
sparkling water or club soda

Tia Black Pearl

I part Tia Maria®
I part Cognac
champagne

Black Hail

2 part Tia Maria®
I part lime or lemon juice
grated chocolate

Tia Mint

I part Tia Maria®
I part creme de menthe

Tia Eggnog

I part Tia Maria®
2 part cognac
2 part milk
I egg beaten
I tsp sugar
grated nutmeg

Sun Trap

I part Tia Maria®
I part Gin
I tbsp lime juice
2 tbsp French vermouth

Jamaica Cow

I part Tia Maria®
2 parts milk

Ice Creams, Parfaits, and Granitas

The tastiest ice creams are made from fresh cream and the very best ingredients, which can be expensive. In the tropics, cream is not always readily available. I suggest using instead a crème anglaise custard base, to which you add the coffee.

Coffee Ice Cream No. 1

This is a simple but delicious ice cream made of cream, coffee and sugar.

2 cups (¾ pint, 500 ml) double cream
1 tbsp instant coffee
2 tbsp hot water
2 oz (50g) sugar

1. Dissolve the instant coffee in 2 tablespoons of hot water and leave to cool.
2. Beat the cream until firm. Add the sugar and cooled coffee.
3. Pour into ice trays (without the dividers) and freeze, beating at intervals to break up the ice crystals that will form. Or place in an ice cream maker.

ENOUGH FOR 6

Coffee Ice Cream No. 2

2 oz (50g) roasted coffee beans
2 cups (¾ pint, 500 ml) milk
4 oz (125g) sugar
6 egg yolks

1. Coarsely crush the beans by placing in a clean dishcloth, beating with a pestle (an electric coffee grinder can also be used).
2. In a saucepan, place the milk and sugar and the crushed coffee beans. Bring to a boil.
3. Remove from heat and leave to infuse for 10–15 minutes. Strain through a fine sieve.
4. Beat the egg yolks and sugar in a bowl. Pour the coffee-milk mixture over the beaten egg yolks and mix well.
5. Pour everything back into the saucepan and heat it over low heat, stirring with a wooden

Left: Caribbean Coconut Pie and Coffee Granita

165

spoon, until the mixture thickens and coats the back of the spoon.

6. Cool. Freeze as directed for Coffee Ice Cream No. I. To make a richer ice cream, substitute single cream for the milk.

ENOUGH FOR 4

Praline Coffee Ice Cream

Follow either recipe for coffee ice cream, but before freezing, add some or all of the praline (recipe given below), finely ground.

Praline

2 oz (50g) blanched almonds
4 oz (125g) sugar

1. Oil a baking sheet. In a heavy-bottomed saucepan, gently heat the sugar, stirring, until dissolved.
2. Add the almonds and stir until the sugar takes on a golden colour or has reached the golden-brown stage (325°F or 160°C).
3. Remove from heat and pour onto the oiled sheet. Allow to cool and harden.
3. Crush with a roller, in a mortar or in a food processor.

Parfaits au Café

There are many types of parfaits made with coffee ice cream and a combination of fruits or liqueurs. These are some of the traditional ones. Feel free to experiment with your favourite flavours and invent new ones.

Parfait Jamaique

Jamaican sugar-loaf pineapple, cubed and soaked in rum
coffee ice cream
whipped cream
Tia Maria® liqueur

1. Place 2 or 3 scoops of coffee ice cream in a parfait dish.
2. Place some of the pineapple on top and around the ice cream.
3. Add whipped cream and pour liqueur over.

SERVES I

Parfait Carnival

freshly grated coconut
coffee ice cream
whipped cream

1. Place 2 or 3 scoops of ice cream in a dessert serving dish.
2. Sprinkle over as much grated coconut as you like.
3. Decorate with whipped cream.

SERVES I

Mango Parfait

Bombay mangoes are the only mangoes that used to be served at table in Jamaica because when they are cut in two, the seed can be easily removed. They are also highly fragrant.

Bombay mangoes, halved, seeds removed
coffee ice cream
whipped cream

Place two halves of a mango on a dessert dish and place a scoop of ice cream in each. Decorate with whipped cream.

SERVES I-2

Rumona Coffee Delight

This is an adaptation of Alex Hawkes's recipe from his Rum Cookbook. He says:
Rumona is a delightfully different Jamaican liqueur, and made from fine quality rum. You will find it is superb when spooned over your favourite ice cream or as an addition to dessert sauces, cakes, icings, puddings and soufflés. It is unique in its special category. Here is an exceptionally showy dessert, guaranteed to intrigue and please your guests.

coffee ice cream
vanilla ice cream
strong black Jamaican coffee, chilled
egg whites, whipped with sugar
Rumona® liqueur
toasted chopped almonds

1. Pour into a tall, cold parfait glass a layer of chilled black Jamaica Blue Mountain® coffee, laced with Rumona®.
2. Add successive layers of vanilla ice cream, egg whites (whipped with a little sugar until almost stiff but not dry) and, finally, a scoop of coffee ice cream.
3. Sprinkle each serving with toasted chopped almonds, pour a splash of Rumona® on top and serve at once.

167

Parfait Caribe

diced Bombay, St Julian or other mangoes
coffee ice cream
whipped cream

Place 2 to 3 scoops of ice cream in a parfait dish. Put a generous amount of diced mangoes over the ice cream and top with whipped cream.

SERVES I

Coffee Granita

5 oz (150g) ground coffee
4 oz (125g) sugar
2 pints (5 cups) water
whipped cream (optional)

1. Place the water and the sugar in a saucepan and bring to a boil.
2. Remove from heat and add the coffee. Cover and leave to infuse and cool. Strain through a fine sieve or muslin.
3. Pour into an ice cream maker or ice trays (without the dividers) and freeze. For the latter, as ice begins to form, beat with a fork to break up the crystals. Repeat at hourly intervals until light, fluffy and frozen. Serve with whipped cream if you like.

SERVES 7-8

Mousses and Soufflés

Cold Mocha Mousse

6 oz (175g) bitter chocolate
¾ pint (500 ml) coffee
6 oz (175g) sugar
6 egg yolks
6 egg whites, stiffly whipped
2 tbsp of Tia Maria® liqueur

1. Melt the chocolate over low heat. Stir in the sugar, then add the coffee.
2. Add the egg yolks one at a time, beating well after each addition.
3. When the sauce begins to thicken, remove it from the heat and add the rum or liqueur. Fold in the whipped egg whites.
4. Pour into individual bowls and chill well before serving.

Cold Coffee Mousse

1 cup (8 fl oz, 250 ml) boiling water
5 tbsp ground coffee
4 oz (125g) sugar
4oz (125g) bitter chocolate
4 eggs, separated
2 tbsp dark rum

1. Pour the boiling water on the coffee and leave to infuse. Strain and add the sugar. Melt the chocolate in a heavy saucepan over low heat.
2. Add the egg yolks one at a time, beating well after each addition. When the mixture begins to thicken, remove from heat and stir in the rum. Whisk the egg whites until stiff and fold into the custard.
3. Pour into individual bowls and cool. Chill well before serving.

ENOUGH FOR 4

Cold Coffee and Ginger Soufflé

1 envelope (¼ oz 12g) unlavoured gelatine
1½ cups (12 oz, 350 ml) cold milk
4 oz (125g) sugar
2 oz (50 ml) Tia Maria®
½ teaspoon Jamaican ginger
4 eggs yolks, lightly beaten
4 egg whites, stiffly beaten.

1. In a saucepan, combine the gelatine and milk. Place over low heat and stir until the gelatine has dissolved.
2. Add the sugar, Tia Maria® and ginger and mix well. Beat the egg yolks lightly and add to the gelatine mixture.
3. Stir until the mixture coats the back of the spoon. Remove from heat and pour into a bowl.
4. Cool and place in the refrigerator. When it begins to set, stir in the stiffly beaten egg whites.

ENOUGH FOR 6

Hot Mocha Soufflé

Proceed as for the Soufflé au Café but add 1 oz (25g) bitter chocolate to the milk-and-coffee mixture and allow to completely melt.

Hot Soufflé au Café

An Haitian recipe for a hot soufflé.

½ liter (1 pint, 2 cups) milk
125g (4 ozs) sugar
1 coffee cup strong coffee
3 tablespoons butter
3 tablespoons flour
4 egg yolks
4 egg whites stiffly beaten
butter, sugar

1. Butter and sugar an ovenproof soufflé dish and set aside. In a heavy saucepan, bring the milk to a boil. Remove from heat and mix in the sugar and coffee.
2. In a medium-size bowl, combine the flour and butter. Pour on the coffee-milk mixture, a little at a time, and mix until smooth.
3. Pour the mixture back into the saucepan and place over low heat, stirring until it thickens.
4. Remove from heat and add the egg yolks, one at a time, beating well with a wooden spoon after each addition.
5. Finally, beat the egg whites stiffly and fold into the mixture. Pour into the buttered soufflé dish and bake in a preheated oven at 400°F (200°C) for 30 minutes or until risen and golden. Serve immediately.

ENOUGH FOR 6

Bavarois and Charlottes

Bavarois au Café

An elegant and delightful dessert for special occasions.

2 cups (¾ pint, 500 ml) milk
4 tbsp ground coffee
5 egg yolks
4 oz (125g) sugar
I tsp vanilla extract
I envelope (¼ oz, I tablespoon) unlavoured gelatine
3 tbsp hot water
I cup (8 fl oz, 250 ml) double cream

1. Bring the milk to a boil with the coffee and leave to infuse for 5 minutes. Strain through double muslin. Whisk the egg yolks in a bowl until they are thick and lemon-coloured.
2. Add the sugar and vanilla. Heat the coffee-milk mixture again, pour it over the eggs yolks and stir. Pour the mixture back into the saucepan and set over low heat.

3. Stir until the mixture thickens and coats the back of a spoon. Beat in the gelatine dissolved in 3 tablespoons of hot water.
4. Pour the mixture into one or several small molds and refrigerate until almost set, then beat in the cream. Leave for at least 3 hours or until firm.

ENOUGH FOR 4.

Charlotte Malakoff

6 oz (175g) unsalted butter
5 oz (150g) sugar
½ cup (4 fl oz, 125 ml) strong coffee
3 oz (75g) ground almonds
3 oz (75g) ground walnuts
I pint (½ liter) double cream
ladyfingers (see recipe below)
Tia Maria® liqueur

1. Oil and line a charlotte mold or a round cake pan with ladyfingers dipped in Tia Maria® liqueur (if using a cake pan, line the bottom with lady fingers.

Left: Charlotte Mocha

173

2. Cream the butter and sugar until lemon-coloured. Add the coffee, ground almonds and walnuts. Beat the double cream until stiff and fold into the butter mixture. Pour into the mould and cover with greaseproof paper cut to the shape of the top of the mould. Chill.
3. If you are using a cake pan, pour half of the mixture over the ladyfingers lining the bottom.
4. Place on top another layer of ladyfingers, topped with the other half of the coffee mixture.
5. Cover with greaseproof paper and chill. To serve, loosen by sliding a knife around the edges of the pan and invert onto a serving dish.

ENOUGH FOR 6.

Ladyfingers

4 eggs, separated
6oz (150g) sugar
5oz (125g) flour
4 oz (100g) conectioner's or icing sugar
piping bag fitted with a 1in (2cm) tube
2 baking trays, buttered and floured

1. Prepare the baking trays and set aside.
2. Separate the eggs. In a medium size bowl, beat the yolks with 5 oz or 125g of the sugar until lemon in colour. Mix in the flour and set aside.
3. Beat the egg whites until stiff, mixing in the remaining 1 oz or 25g of sugar. Pour the yolk mixture into the whites and quickly fold in. Pour into a piping bag fitted with the tube and pipe the mixture unto the baking trays, making fingers of about 3½ inches or 9cm in length.
4. Powder them with icing sugar and bake at 350°F or 180°C for 18–20 minutes.

MAKES APROXIMATELY 20 LADYFINGERS

Charlotte Russe

This is a lighter, frothier dessert than Charlotte Malakoff which is made heavier with the addition of nuts.

2 cups (¾ pint, 500 ml) milk
4 tbsp (1 oz, 50g) ground coffee
5 egg yolks
4 oz (125g) sugar
1 tsp vanilla extract
1 envelope (¼ oz, 8g) unflavoured gelatine
1 cup (8 oz, 250 ml) double cream
ladyfingers (see Charlotte Malakoff)
coffee liqueur

1. Line an oiled charlotte mould with ladyfingers dipped in coffee liqueur.
2. Make a Bavarois custard (follow instructions for Bavarois au Café page 173) from the above ingredients.
3. Pour in the custard and top with greaseproof paper cut to fit the mould. Chill for at least 3 hours. Invert on a serving dish.

SERVES 6

Charlotte Mocha

4 tbsp (1 oz, 50g) ground coffee
2 cups (¾ pint, 500 ml) milk
½ teaspoon unflavoured gelatine
2 tbsp hot water
3 egg yolks
4 oz (125g) sugar
2 oz (50g) flour, sifted
½ tsp vanilla extract
2 oz (50g) bitter chocolate
ladyfingers (see Charlotte Malakoff)
coffee liqueur
whipped cream (optional)

1. Mix the ground coffee into milk and heat the mixture. Remove from heat as it comes to a boil, and leave to infuse for 10 minutes.

2. Strain through double muslin and add ½ teaspoon gelatine mixed with 2 tablespoons hot water.
3. Melt the chocolate in a saucepan, add milk-gelatine mixture and heat again, stirring to dissolve the gelatine.
4. Place the egg yolks and sugar in a bowl. Whisk until the mixture becomes pale yellow, then add the sifted flour and mix well. Add the coffee–milk mixture little by little, mixing well.
5. Pour this mixture back into the saucepan and place over low heat. Whisk until it thickens. Remove from heat and leave to cool slightly.
6. Pour into a charlotte mold lined with ladyfingers dipped in coffee liqueur. Cover with greaseproof paper cut to fit the top, and chill until firm.
7. Turn out on a serving dish and decorate with whipped cream if you wish.

ENOUGH FOR 4

175

Choux and Brioches

This is a circular ring of baked choux pastry that is cut in half—that is, into 2 rings—and filled with coffee pastry cream.

I cup (8 fl oz, 250 ml) water
I tbsp instant coffee
½ cup (100g, 4 oz) butter
½ tsp sugar
5 oz (150g) all-purpose flour, sifted
5 eggs
almond flakes

1. Bring the water, coffee, butter, salt and sugar to a boil in a heavy saucepan, allowing the butter to completely melt. As soon as the mixture starts to boil, remove it from heat; add the sifted flour and mix vigorously with a wooden spoon until the batter is smooth.

2. Return it to medium heat and stir constantly for 5 minutes. Turn off the heat and add 4 eggs, one at a time, mixing vigorously after each addition. Break the last egg into a small bowl and whisk lightly.

3. Add this beaten egg, a little at a time, to the batter until it is smooth, thick and satiny and makes a 'plop' when dropped from the spoon. It may not be necessary to add all of the last egg, depending upon the type of flour used.

4. Place the mixture in a piping bag with a large nozzle. Grease and flour a baking sheet. Then squeeze out 3 large rings, 8 to10 inches in diameter, onto the baking sheet.

5. After you have made the first ring, make the second either just inside or just outside of the first, then pipe the third ring into a second layer, covering the seam between the first and second. Brush with the beaten egg and sprinkle with almond flakes.

6. Bake in a preheated oven at 400–425°F (200–225°C) for 15 minutes, then lower the heat to 375°F (190°C) and bake for 30–40 more minutes. Turn off the heat and

Left: Paris Brest au Café

prop the oven door slightly ajar with a wooden spoon to allow the pastry to further dry out. When quite dry, remove from the oven.

7. Cut into 2 rings and fill with Crème Patissière au Café (page 195). (Alternatively, you can make smaller rings and fill them with the pastry cream.)

SERVES 6

Coffee Brioche

1 lb (500g) flour
1 oz (20g) fresh yeast
1 tbsp instant coffee dissolved in 3 tbsp water
½ tsp salt
6 eggs
½ lb (250g) softened butter

Making dough by hand

1. Place the flour in a large bowl or on a marble slab. Make a well in the centre and add the yeast and the coffee mixed with water. Mix in well, then add the sugar and 5 of the eggs. Mix from the centre outward, incorporating the flour. Beat the last egg and add to the dough, little by little, if necessary—the mixture must not be runny but must hold its form. This can be tested by spooning up some of the mixture and dropping it back in the bowl. If you hear a 'plop', the mixture is ready. If still runny, mix in a little more egg. Add the butter and work the dough by pulling it towards you and throwing it outward while kneading with the base of your palm. Continue kneading until the dough takes on a satiny appearance. Sprinkle it with some flour and leave it to rise to half again its size, then knead again.

2. Remove a small piece of the dough and shape it into a blob with a tail. Place the rest in an oiled brioche mould. Make a small hole in the centre and dampen inside the hole. Insert the small piece of dough and lightly press it into place. Leave the dough to rise until it is increased by half it's size again, then knead .

3. Brush with beaten egg and bake at 425°F (220°C) for 15–20 minutes. For large brioches, reduce the heat to 375°F (190°C) and bake for another 10 minutes or until brown.

Making dough in bread machine

4. The dough can be made quite successfully in the bread machine using the dough hook. Place the flour, yeast and coffee in a bowl and mix. Add the sugar and eggs, one at a time. Finally, add the softened butter and mix until the dough has a satiny finish. Let it rise as in the hand method and finish as described.

ENOUGH FOR 6

Coffee Crèmes

Crème Caramel au Café

Caramel
½ cup (4 oz , 100g) granulated sugar
¼ cup (2 fl oz) water

Crème or Custard
4 cups (1½ pint, 1 liter) milk
4 tbsp ground coffee
5 eggs, lightly beaten
sugar
ovenproof custard dishes
whipped cream

1. To make the caramel, put the sugar and water in a small heavy saucepan. Stir and bring to a boil. Boil until the sugar is thick and golden brown. Divide the caramel evenly among the individual custard dishes and set aside.

2. For the custard, heat the milk and ground coffee just until it comes to the boil. Remove from heat and stir in the sugar. Leave for 5–10 minutes. Strain through a double muslin cloth and set aside.

3. Beat the eggs in a large bowl. Add the strained coffee-milk mixture. Pour mixture through a sieve into individual custard dishes.

4. Place custard dishes in a roasting pan and add water to halfway up the sides of the dishes. Bake at 325°F (160°C) for 40–45 minutes or until set. Test by inserting a knife in the centre; if it comes out clean, the custard is done. Cool and then chill. Garnish with whipped cream and turn out onto individual dessert dishes .

ENOUGH FOR 6

Coffee Spiced Crème Caramel

Caramel
½ cup (4 oz, 125g) granulated sugar
4 tbsp water

Crème or Custard
2 cups (¾ pint, 500 ml) milk
6 cardamom pods
2-inch (2.5cm) piece cinnamon stick
4 tbsp sugar
½ cup (8fl oz, 250 ml) strong black coffee
5 egg yolks
whipped cream (optional)

1. To coat the bottom of the custard dishes with caramel, place the ½ cup (125g) sugar and water in a small heavy saucepan. Heat gently until the sugar dissolves, then increase the heat. Boil until the sugar thickens and becomes golden in colour. Remove from the heat and pour a little of the caramel in each dish (or coat one large dish). Set aside.
2. In another saucepan, place the cinnamon stick and the cardamom pods. Pour the milk over them and bring it to a boil. Remove from heat and stir in 4 tablespoons sugar. Let stand for about 10 minutes. Strain and add the coffee.
3. In a bowl, lightly beat the egg yolks. Pour in the hot spiced coffee-milk mixture and mix well.
4. Pour into custard dishes and place in a roasting pan with water halfway up the sides of the dishes. Bake at 300°F (150°C) for 40–45 minutes or until done. Test by inserting a knife in the centre; if it comes out clean, the custard is done. Cool, then refrigerate.
5. Turn out onto serving dishes and add whipped cream if desired.

ENOUGH FOR 5

Coffee Jelly

2 cups (¾ pint, 500 ml) strong hot coffee
1 envelope (¼ oz, 5g) unflavoured gelatine
sugar to taste
1 cup whipping cream

Add sugar to the hot coffee, sprinkle the gelatine over it, and mix until the sugar and gelatine are completely dissolved. Pour into custard dishes and chill until set. De-mold by dipping briefly in warm water, and place on a serving dish. Whip the cream and garnish the jelly. Alternatively, the cream can be mixed into the jelly when it is half set.

ENOUGH FOR 4

181

Coffee Rum Crème

2 cups (¾ pint, 500ml) milk
1 tsp vanilla extract
4 egg yolks
3 tbsp sugar
½ cup (4 fl oz, 125 ml) strong coffee
2 tbsp rum

Bring the milk to a boil and add the vanilla. Remove from heat. In a bowl, beat the egg yolks lightly. Add the sugar and mix. Pour in the hot milk, then the coffee and rum. Pour into custard dishes and set in a roasting pan with water halfway up the sides of the dishes. Bake at 300°F (160°C) for 40–45 minutes or until done. Test by inserting a knife in the centre; if it comes out clean, the custard is done. Cool, then chill. Serve in individual custard dishes.

ENOUGH FOR 4

Cakes

Coffee Rum Cake

2½ cups (15 oz, 435g) flour, sifted
½ tsp salt
2 tbsp baking powder
1 cup (6 oz, 175g) brown sugar
½ cup (4 oz, 100g) butter
3 eggs
1 cup (8 fl oz, 250 ml) strong coffee
3 tbsp rum
1 cup (8 fl oz, 250 ml) milk
coffee liqueur

1. In a bowl, sift the flour, salt and baking powder. In another bowl, cream the sugar and butter, then add the eggs, one at a time, mixing well after each addition. Add the flour mixture alternately with the coffee, rum and milk.
2. Pour into a greased 9-inch baking container. Bake at 350°F (180°C) for 50–60 minutes or until done. When cool, turn out of the tin and sprinkle with coffee liqueur.

SERVES 6-8

Coffee-Cinnamon Cake

1 cup (6 oz, 175g) brown sugar
½ cup (4 oz, 125g) butter
3 eggs
2 cups (12 oz, 300g) flour
1 tbsp baking powder
½ teaspoon salt
1 tbsp powdered cinnamon
1 cup (8 fl oz, 250 ml) milk
1 cup (8 fl oz, 250 ml) strong coffee

Cream the sugar and butter. Add the eggs one at a time, then the flour, baking powder, salt and cinnamon, alternately with the milk mixed with the coffee. Pour into a greased 9-inch (22.86 cm) baking tin and bake in a preheated oven at 350°F (180°C) for 45–60 minutes or until done. When cool, turn the cake out of the tin, cut horizontally into two pieces, and fill with Coffee Butter Filling, below.

SERVES 6-8

Previous Page: Coffee Sweet-Potato Gateau

Left: Coffee Rum Cake

Mocha Cake No. 1

1 ½ cups (12 oz, 375g) sugar
½ cup (4 oz, 125g) butter
3 egg yolks
½ cup (4 fl oz, 125 ml) milk
½ cup (4 fl oz, 125 ml) strong coffee
2 oz (50g) chocolate, melted
2 cups (12 ozs, 350g) flour
1 tbsp vanilla
3 egg whites, stiffly beaten
icing sugar

1. Butter a cake tin and set aside.
2. Beat the butter and sugar with a wooden spoon until light and fluffy. Add the eggs, one at a time, and mix well.
3. Add the milk and coffee to the melted chocolate and add mixture to the batter. Mix well, then add the flour and vanilla. Finally, fold in the stiffly beaten egg whites and pour the batter into the greased cake tin. Bake in a preheated oven at 350°F (180°C) for about 45 minutes or until done. Cool on a rack. While still warm, slide a knife around the sides of the cake and invert onto a dish. Dust the top with icing sugar.

Mocha Cake No. 2

1 cup (8fl oz, 250 ml) strong coffee
2 oz (50g) bitter chocolate, melted
½ cup (4 fl oz, 125 ml) milk
1 cup (8 oz, 250g) sugar
½ cup (4 oz, 100g) butter
3 eggs
2 cups (12 oz, 350g) flour
2 tbsp baking powder
½ tsp salt

1. Mix the melted chocolate with the coffee and milk, and set aside. Cream the sugar and butter. Add the milk and coffee to the melted chocolate and set aside. Blend in the flour, baking powder and salt to the egg, sugar and butter mixture. Lastly add the chocolate, coffee, milk mixture. Pour into a 9-inch (22.86m) baking pan. Bake in a preheated oven at 350°F (180°C) for 50–60 minutes or until done. Cool on a rack.
2. While still slightly warm, loosen edges of the cake with a knife. Turn out onto a serving dish and sprinkle with icing sugar.

Coffee–Sweet Potato Gateau

4 oz (125g) butter
8 oz (250g) sugar
1 cup (200ml) strong coffee
2 cups (¾ pint, 500 ml) milk
1 tsp grated nutmeg
1 tsp vanilla
2 lb (1 kg) sweet potato, grated
3 eggs

Preheat the oven to 350°F (180°C) and grease a 9-inch baking tin (22.86cm). Cream the butter and sugar. Add the coffee, milk, nutmeg and vanilla and mix thoroughly. Add the grated sweet potato and mix well, then add the eggs, one at a time, mixing well after each addition. Bake at 350°F (180°C) for 45–60 minutes or until done. Serve with Mocha Sauce (page 197)

Serves 7–8

Coffee Butter Filling

3 oz (75g) butter
1 egg
3 oz (75g) icing sugar
1 tbsp instant coffee granules

Cream the butter, add the egg, then the icing sugar and the instant coffee granules. Beat well until fluffy.

Pies, Cakes and Cookies

Coffee Cheesecake

Crust
8 oz (250g) cookies, finely crushed
4 oz (½ cup, 125g) butter, melted
9-inch (22.86 cm) pie tin

Mix the cookie crumbs with the melted butter. Spread the mixture in the bottom and up the sides of the pie tin. Set aside.

Filling

1 lb (500g) cream cheese
4 oz (100g) sugar
3 eggs, beaten
4 oz (100g) flour, sifted
4 tbsp Tia Maria®
or Sangsters Coffee® Liqueur
brown sugar

Beat the cream cheese with a wooden spoon until it is soft. Beat in the sugar and the eggs, one at a time, then the flour and the coffee liqueur. Scrape the mixture into the pie shell and smooth the top. Sprinkle with brown sugar and bake in an oven preheated to 400°F (200°C) for 30 minutes or until firm. Cool and then refrigerate. Serve cold.

ENOUGH FOR 6

Caribbean Coconut Pie

Pie shell
1 cup (6 oz, 150g) flour, sifted
¼ tsp salt
⅓ (3 oz, 75 g) cold butter, cubed
iced water

Place the flour and salt in a bowl and mix well. Using your fingers, mix the butter into the flour, working quickly. If the dough is sticky, add a little more flour. Wrap in plastic and refrigerate until needed, then roll out and line a pie dish.

Left: Coffee Cheesecake

189

Pie Filling
4 eggs
½ cup (4 oz, 125g) sugar
pinch of salt
¾ cup (5 oz, 130g) flour
½ cup (4 fl oz, 125ml) strong coffee
I cup (8 fl oz, 250 ml) milk
I tsp vanilla
2 cups (8 oz, 150g) grated coconut

In a bowl, beat the eggs lightly, add the sugar and salt, then the flour, coffee, milk and vanilla. Mix well. Lastly, stir in the grated coconut. Scrape the filling into the prepared pastry shell and bake at 350°F (180°C) for 40–45 minutes or until the top is brown. Cool before serving.

SERVES 6–8

Middle Eastern Shortcakes

I lb (500g) softened butter
6 oz (175g) sugar
I tbsp instant coffee granules
I lb flour (500g) sifted.

Using a wooden spoon, vigorously mix the butter, sugar and instant coffee granules. Add the flour and mix well, kneading lightly and quickly by hand. Make little balls of the dough and place them on baking sheets (do not grease or flour as the mixture is high in fat), allowing some space for expansion. Flatten them slightly and prick the tops all over with a fork. Bake immediately in a preheated oven at 350°F (180°C) for 15–20 minutes. They should remain pale, as browning will harden them. Remove from the oven at once. When cool, sprinkle them with icing sugar.

MAKES 15–20

Right: Turkish Coffee and Middle Eastern Shortcake

Coffee Macaroons

6 oz (175g) ground almonds
4 oz (125g) sugar
2 egg whites
2 tbsp strong coffee
icing sugar

Butter and flour a baking sheet and set aside. In a bowl, mix the almonds and sugar. Beat in the egg whites and the coffee. The mixture should be soft but not runny. Drop by spoonfuls on the baking sheet, allowing enough space for the macaroons to expand. Sprinkle with icing sugar and bake in a preheated oven at 350°F (180°C) for 20 minutes or until golden in colour.

MAKES 20

Ginger-Coffee Biscuits

½ cup (4 oz, 125g) sugar
4 egg yolks
1 tbsp grated Jamaican ginger
2 tbsp strong coffee
½ cup (4 oz, 100g) flour
4 egg whites, stiffly beaten

Oil and flour baking sheet(s) and set aside. In a bowl, using a wooden spoon or a whisk, beat the sugar and egg yolks until lemon-coloured. Blend in the ginger, coffee and flour. Fold in the stiffly beaten egg whites. Place by spoonfuls on baking sheets, leaving enough space between individual cookies for expansion. If you prefer, the mixture can be piped into sticks or other shapes. Bake in a preheated oven at 350°F (180°C) for 15–20 minutes or until brown.

MAKES 15-20

Candy

Coffee Fudge

8 oz (250 ml) evaporated milk
2 oz (50 ml) strong coffee
1 lb (500g) brown sugar
2 oz (50g) butter

Butter a shallow 8-inch square baking container. Set aside. In a heavy saucepan, combine the evaporated milk, coffee and sugar. Heat over low heat and stir until the sugar has dissolved. Add the butter and stir. Increase the heat to medium, stirring from time to time, until the mixture thickens to the soft-ball stage. Test by dropping a little of the mixture in some cold water. If it forms a little ball, then it is done. Alternatively, test with a candy thermometer for a temperature of 240°F (115°C). Pour the mixture into the greased container and cool. When it is firm but still warm, mark the fudge into squares. Cut through and separate when cold.

Makes a pound (500g) of fudge

Rum-Coffee Fudge

½ cup (125ml) milk
1 tbsp rum
1 tbsp instant coffee granules
1 lb (500g) granulated sugar
2 oz (50g) butter
nuts or raisins (optional)

Butter a shallow 8-inch (20.32cm) square container and set aside. Pour the milk into a large, heavy saucepan. Add the instant coffee, rum, and nuts or raisins and place over low heat. Stir until the sugar is dissolved, then increase the heat to medium and boil until the mixture forms a soft ball when tested in cold water (240°F or 115°C on a candy thermometer). Remove from heat and stir well. Pour into the greased container and cool. When it is almost set, mark into squares. When cold, break apart into individual squares.

Makes a pound (500g) of fudge

Mocha Coconut Truffles

8 oz (250g) bitter chocolate, chopped
6 tbsp strong coffee
4 oz (125g) butter
6 oz (175g) icing sugar
I cup (4 oz, 125g) grated coconut

Place the chopped chocolate and the coffee in the top of a double boiler or in a bowl set in hot water, and heat. When the chocolate has melted, remove it from the heat and beat in the butter and icing sugar until smooth. Cool, then chill in the refrigerator for about 30 minutes or until it is firm enough to handle. Make small balls from it and dip each in the grated coconut. Chill again until hard.

MAKES 15

Frostings and Fillings

Coffee Butter Frosting

4 oz (100g) butter
2 cups (1lb, 500g) sifted flour
2 oz (50g) strong coffee

Beat the sugar and butter until light and
fluffy. Add the coffee a little at a time until
the required consistency is reached. Use as
a frosting or filling for cakes.

ENOUGH FOR 1 CAKE

Mocha Frosting

4 oz (100g) bitter chocolate
2 cups (1lb,500g) icing sugar
2 fl oz (50ml) strong coffee

Melt the chocolate, broken into small
pieces, in a heavy saucepan over low heat.
Slowly mix in the icing sugar and the coffee.
Remove from heat and use to frost cakes
and other pastries.

ENOUGH FOR 1 CAKE

Coffee Chantilly

2 cups (3/4 pint, 500ml) heavy cream
2 oz (50g) sugar
2 tbsp strong coffee
½ tsp vanilla

Whip the cream with the sugar until very
thick. Add the coffee and the vanilla. Use
as a filling or decoration for any dessert.

ENOUGH FOR 1 CAKE.

Crème Patissière au Cafe

This is a standard filling for many pastries and cakes.

4 tbsp (1oz, 20g) strong coffee
2 cups (1pint, 500 ml) heavy cream
3 egg yolks
4 oz (100g) sugar
2 oz (50g) flour, sifted
½ tsp vanilla

Stir ground coffee into the milk and heat, removing from heat as it comes to a boil. Leave to infuse for 10 minutes. Strain through a double muslin cloth. Return to saucepan over low heat and keep hot. Place the egg yolks and sugar in a bowl and whisk until the mixture is pale yellow in colour, then add the sifted flour and mix well. Add the coffee-milk mixture, mixing well. Pour the mixture back into the saucepan and place over low heat. Whisk until it thickens. Remove from heat and pour into a bowl. Smear the top with butter to prevent it from crusting. Cool, then refrigerate until ready for use.

ENOUGH FOR 2 SETS PASTRY

Sweet Sauces

These sauces will enhance a piece of pie, cake or pastry or a scoop of ice cream.

Coffee Rum Sauce

2 egg yolks
1 cup (8oz, 250g) sugar
1½ cups hot strong coffee
2 tbsp butter
2 tbsp rum or coffee liqueur

The method is the same as if you were making a pastry cream. Beat the egg yolks with the sugar and add the hot coffee. Pour into a saucepan and heat over low heat. Stir constantly until the mixture thickens. Mix in the butter and rum. Serve at once.

Mocha Sauce

4 oz (100g) sweet chocolate
1 tsp cornstarch
1 tbsp instant coffee granules
3 tbsp water
1 oz (25g) butter

Melt the chocolate in a bowl over hot water or in a saucepan over low heat. Combine the coffee and the cornstarch and dissolve in the water. Pour this mixture into the melted chocolate. Mix well and add the butter. Serve hot on pastries such as profiteroles and on other cakes, pastries, puddings or ice cream.

ENOUGH FOR ONE CAKE

Butterscotch Coffee Sauce

1 cup (8 fl oz, 250 ml) milk
4 tbsp brown sugar
1 tbsp cornstarch
1 tbsp instant coffee
1 tbsp butter

In a small saucepan, combine milk, sugar, cornstarch and instant coffee. Place over low heat and stir until the mixture thickens and coats the back of a spoon. Remove from heat and blend in butter. Serve hot over cakes, pastries, ice cream or puddings.

Meat Sauces

Italian Meat Sauce

2 oz (50g) butter or oil
2 cloves garlic, chopped
I onion, chopped
½ lb (500g) ground beef
I tbsp flour
2 tbsp tomato paste
½ lb (500g) mushrooms, chopped
2 tbsp chopped parsley
2 cups (¾ pint, 500 ml) coffee
salt and pepper to taste

In a heavy saucepan, lightly brown the garlic
and onion in the oil or butter. Add ground
beef and brown. Blend in the flour, then
add the tomato paste, mushrooms, parsley
and coffee. Add salt and pepper. Simmer
for 30 minutes. The sauce should not be
too thick or too thin.

ENOUGH FOR 4

Jerk Barbecue Sauce

2 tbsp oil
2 tbsp Walkerswood jerk sauce
2 tbsp tomato paste
I cup (8fl oz) strong coffee

Heat oil in a small pan and add the jerk
sauce and tomato paste. Mix, then add the
coffee. Remove from heat and cool. Brush
onto any meat, poultry or fish.

Main Courses

Island Braised Beef

4 tbsp oil
3 lb (1¼ kg) stewing beef, cubed
2 cloves garlic, chopped
2 onions, chopped
2 bay leaves
sprig of thyme
½ lb (500g) carrots, sliced
I bottle beer
I cup (8fl oz, 250 ml) black coffee
salt and pepper

Heat the oil in a heavy braising saucepan and brown the meat on all sides. Add the garlic and chopped onions and stir for a few minutes until the onions have softened. Add the carrots, bay leaves and thyme. Stir well and add the beer and coffee. Season with salt and pepper. Bring to a boil, then lower heat and braise until tender—about 2 hours.

ENOUGH FOR 6–7

Beef à la Bourguignonne

4 tbsp oil
2 oz (50g) bacon, diced
2 onions, chopped
2 cloves garlic, chopped
3 lb (1¼ kg) stewing beef, cubed
2 tbsp flour
2 cups (8fl oz, 250 ml) red wine
I cup (8 fl oz, 250 ml) strong coffee
bouquet garni (thyme, parsley, bay leaves)
salt and pepper to taste
½ lb (250g) button mushrooms-sliced if large
ENOUGH FOR 6–7

Heat oil in a heavy braising pan. Fry the bacon pieces lightly with the onions. Remove from the pan and set aside. Add the garlic to the pan and fry for a few seconds, then add the cubed meat and brown quickly. Add flour and stir well until it has amalgamated with the juices and oil

Left: Island Braised Beef

201

in the pan. Pour in the wine and coffee, add the bouquet garni (tied with a string in a muslin bag) and season with salt and pepper. Cover and simmer until almost ready—about 1½ to 2 hours—then add the fried onions, bacon and raw mushrooms. Cook for a further 15–30 minutes. Before serving, remove the bouquet garni.

Creole Pot Roast

Marinade

3 stalks escallion or spring onions, chopped
1 small tomato, chopped fine
1 tsp fresh thyme leaves
2 slices hot pepper, chopped
½ tsp ground allspice
salt and pepper

Mix all ingredients in a bowl and set aside.

Roast preparation

3 tbsp oil
3 lb (1¼ kg) braising beef
2 cloves garlic, chopped
2 onions, chopped
2 tomatoes, chopped
2 sweet peppers, chopped
sprig of thyme
1 cup (8 fl oz, 250 ml) rum
2 cups (¾ pint, 500 ml) strong coffee
salt and pepper

With a sharp knife, make slits all over the meat. Into each slit, insert a pinch of the marinade. Scrape any remaining marinade onto the meat and rub in. Leave for at least 2 hours. Heat the oil in a heavy braising pan large enough to hold the meat. Add meat and brown on all sides. Remove meat from the pan. In the same oil in the pan, sauté the garlic and onions, then add the tomatoes, peppers and thyme. Pour in the rum and coffee and add salt and pepper to taste. Return the browned meat to the pan. Cover and braise until tender (about 2 hours), adding a little water if necessary.

ENOUGH FOR 6–7

Equivalents

Liquids

¼ cup	2 fluid ounces	50 millilitres (ml)
½ cup	4 fl oz	125–150 ml
1 cup	8 fl oz (½ pint)	250 ml
1½ cups	12 fl oz	350 ml
2 cups	16 fl oz (1 pint)	500 ml
3 cups	1-1/2 pt	600 ml
4 cups	1 quart	1 litre (L)
8 cups	2 qt	2.5 L

Solids

1 oz	25 grams (g)
2 oz	50 g
3 oz	75 g
4 oz	100–125 g
5 oz	150 g
6 oz	175 g
8 oz	250 g
1 lb	500 g
2 lb	1.1 kilograms (kg)
5 lb	2.25 kg

Principal Solid Ingredients

Flour	I cup	5–6 oz	150–175g
White sugar	I cup	6 oz	175 g
Brown Sugar	I cup	8 oz	250g
Butter/margarine	I cup	8 oz	250g
Raisins	I cup	6 oz	175g

Oven Temperature

Fahrenheit (°)	Centigrade (°)	Gas	Heat of oven
225	110	—	Very cool
250	130	—	Very cool
275	140	I	Cool
300	150	2	Cool
325	160	3	Moderate
350	180	4	Moderate
375	190	5	Fairly hot
400	200	6	Fairly hot
425	220	7	Hot
450	230	8	Very hot
475	240	9	Very hot

Appendices

Survey Maps and Plans of Blue Mountain Coffee Estates

These may be found at the National Library of Jamaica

ARNTULLY

ISN 1120-S.T.T.69

A plan of the estate with coffee fields theron in the Parish of St Thomas the prop. of Charles Lascelles 1860.

BELLEVUE

**S.T. A 126—BEAUTIFUL V. LARGE, with barbecues, house, huts

A plan of the coffee fields of Resource and Bellevue plantations in the parish of Pt. Royal in possession of William Chisholm Esq. at whose request this survey has been performed in March 1859 by Felix Harrison for Thomas Harrison. crown surveyor, Surrey.

**S.T.A. 278—Very good map and condition.

Diagram represents within the Blue lines the boundaries of Bellevue plantation in Port Royal the property of Henry Kent containing 274 acres and formerly belonging to Mrs F.S. Strupar. Performed in April 1848 by McGleachy and Griffiths.

CHARLOTTENBURG

* S.T.A.235—Several parcels inc. this plantation

COLD SPRING

** S.T.225—Very good, coffee & gt. House

Diagram represents Cold spring plantation with sub divisions.

** S.T.203

Diagram represents C. spring plan circumscribed with red lines, now belonging to the proprietor of Clifton Mount surveyed Oct. 1830 by McGleachy and Smith.

MAVIS BANK

** S.T.363 (1808)

MIDDLETON/MERRYMANS HILL

** S.T.A.947 MIDDLETON *& MERRYMANS HILL CHART OF COFFEE FIELDS

* S.T.A.1513

(MIDDLETON)—v. Good, coffee trees, huts house though in BAD CONDITION.

Diagram represents a plan of Middleton and Merrymans Hill plantations the property of the Duke of Buckingham and Chandos, surveyed by desire of the Hon. Richard Barrett in 1835 by Morris Cuninghame & Woolridge.

STRAWBERRY HILL

***   S.T.A.258

Very good, coloured, fields and buildings

Diagram shows S. Hill with divisions showing field pieces and buildings.

RESOURCE PLANTATION

**S.T.A 116

Lovely little coloured map of coffee fields

A plan of the coffee pieces of Resource Plantation in the Port Royal Mountains surveyed by William Buchanan in March 1858 by request of William Chisholm Esq.

Licensed Coffee Roasters and Exporters

Roasters

1. Blue Mahoe Estates Jamaica Limited
   28 Lancaster Road
   Kingston 10

2. City of Refuge Children's Home
   Content Gap
   Gordon Town P.A.
   St. Andrew

3. Coffee Industries Limited
   17 Barbados Avenue
   Kingston 5

4. Coffee Roasters of Jamaica Limited
   Unit 3
   69-75 Constant Spring Road
   Kingston 10

5. Coffee Solutions
   33 Lyndhurst Road
   Kingston 5

6. Greenwich Mountain Estate Limited
   1A South Camp Road
   Kingston 4

7. J. Wray & Nephew Limited
   234 Spanish Town Road
   Kingston 11

8. Jablum Jamaica Limited
   Mavis Bank
   St. Andrew

9. Jamaica Standard Products Company
   Limited
   Williamsfield
   Manchester

10. Salada Foods Jamaica Limited
    20 Bell Road
    Kingston 11

11. Wallenford Coffee Company Limited
    Marcus Garvey Drive
    Kingston 13

Exporters

1. Blue Mahoe Estates Jamaica Limited
   28 Lancaster Road
   Kingston 10

2. Blue Mountain Coffee Cooperative
   Society Limited
   Cedar Valley
   St. Thomas

3. Blue Mountain Coffee Venture Limited
   3 Haughton Avenue
   Kingston 10

4. Clifton Mount Estate Limited
   214 Marcus Garvey Drive
   Kingston 13

5. Coffee Industries Limited
   17 Barbados Avenue
   Kingston 5

6. Coffee Roasters of Jamaica Limited
   Unit 3
   Blaise Industrial Park
   69-75 Constant Spring Road
   Kingston 10

7. Coffee Traders Limited
   214 Marcus Garvey Drive
   Kingston 13

8. Gold Cup Coffee Company Limited
   Unit 3
   Blaise Industrial Park
   69-75 Constant Spring Road
   Kingston 10

9. Greenwich Mountain Estate Limited
   1A South Camp Road
   Kingston 4

10. J. Wray & Nephew Limited
    234 Spanish Town Road
    Kingston 11

11. Jablum Jamaica Limited
    Mavis Bank
    St. Andrew

12. Jamaica Coffee Corporation Limited
    90 Hope Road
    Kingston 6

13. Jamaica Standard Products Limited
    Williamsfield
    Manchester

14. Mavis Bank Central Factory Limited
    Mavis Bank
    St. Andrew

15. Nipon Farms Limited
    39 Hagley Park Road
    Kingston 10

16. RSW Estates Limited
    31 Upper Waterloo Road
    Kingston 10

17. Salada Foods Jamaica   Limited
    20 Bell Road
    Kingston 11

18. Supreme Jamaica Coffee Corporation
    Limited
    188 Spanish Town Road
    Kingston 11

19. Wallenford Coffee Company Limited
    Marcus Garvey Drive
    Kingston 13

Bibliography

Bigelow, John. *Jamaica in 1850*: or the effects of sixteen years of Freedom on a slave colony. New York & London: George G. Putnam, 1851.

Boerhaave, Herman. *Index Alter Plantarum quae in Horto Academico Lugduno-Batavo aluntur.* Leyden: the Author & P. vander Aa, 1720.

Budhlall, Penelope. *Growing Coffee in Jamaica*. Kingston: Coffee Industry Development Company, 1986.

Cargill, Morris. *Jamaica Farewell.* Seaucus, NJ: Lyle Stuart Inc, 1978.

Cassidy, F.G. *Jamaica Talk: Three Hundred Years of the English Language in Jamaica.* London: MacMillan Education Ltd., 1961.

Coffee-Early Works to 1800. Letter on the advantage of Cultivating Coffee and Cocoa in the British Sugar Island. University of the West Indies Library, Mona, Kingston, Jamaica.

Coffee Industry Board: Coffee. Pamphlet.

Coffee. Jamaica Agricultural Society, 1963. Pamphlet.

Cohen, Steve. *On the Trade of the Blue Mountain Coffee.* Pamphlet. 1985. University of the West Indies Library, Mona, Kingston, Jamaica.

Corrie, Edgar. Letters on the subject of the duties on coffee, 1808. National Library of Jamaica, Kingston.

Davids, Kenneth. *Coffee: A Guide to the Buying, Brewing and Enjoying.* 5th edition. New York: St. Martin's Griffin, 2001.

Department of Public Gardens and Plantations. Agronomy Section, Hope Gardens, Kingston, Jamaica.

D'Israeli, Isaac. *Curiosities of Literature*. London: George Routledge and sons, 1866.

Edwards, Bryan. *The history, civil and commercial of the British colonies in the West Indies*, Vol. I. London: John Stockdale, 1819, 190.

Ellis, John. *An Historical Account of Coffee with an Engraving and Botanical Description of the Tree: To Which Are Added Sundry Papers Relative to Its Culture and Use, as an Article of Diet and of Commerce*. London: printed for Edward and Charles Dilly, 1774.

Fourness, Allen. *The Jamaica Coffee Boom and John Mackeson—A Blue Mountain Coffee Planter, 1807– 1819*. Pamphlet. National Library of Jamaica, Kingston.

Goldsmith, Arthur. *Commodity Associations and Agricultural Production in Jamaica*. Kingston: Coffee Industry Board, 1983.

Hall, Douglas. *Free Jamaica*. New Haven: Yale University Press, 1959.

Hickey, William. *Memoirs of William Hickey*, ed. Alfred Spencer. London: Hurst & Blackett, 1948.

Higman, Barry W. *Jamaica Surveyed. Plantation maps and plans of the eighteenth and nineteenth centuries*. Kingston: Institute of Jamaica, 1988.

Kelly, James. *Jamaica in 1831: Being a Narrative of Seventeen Years' Residence in that Island*. Pamphlet. Belfast. 1838, 1st ed. (National Library of Jamaica, Kingston).

Laws, Statutes of Great Britain. An Act for the further encouraging of Coffee and coconuts in His Majesty's Islands and Plantations of America, 1811.

Laborie, P.J. *The Coffee Planter of Saint Domingo*. London: T. Cadell and W. Davis, 1798.

Lim, Bea. Letter to the editor. *Daily Gleaner*. Month day, 1992.

Lloyd Reginald. *Twentieth Century Impressions of the West Indies: Their History, People, Commerce, Industries and Resources*. Lloyd's Greater Britain Publishing Co. Ltd. London, England, 1914.

Lowndes, John. *The Coffee Planter, or an Essay on the Cultivation and Manufacturing of the Article of West Indian Produce*. London: C. Lowndes, 1807.

Long, Edward. *The History of Jamaica, or A General Survey of the Ancient and Modern State of that Island*. Vol 3. London: Printed for T. Lowndes, 1774.

Mackley, Lesley. *A Gourmet's Guide to Coffee and Tea*. New York: HP Books, 1989.

McCoy, Elin, and John F. Walker. *Coffee and Tea*. New American Library, 1988.

Middleton and Merryman's Field Coffee Plantations and Letters. Stowe Papers, Huntington Library. Microfilm, University of the West Indies Library, Mona, Kingston, Jamaica.

Moseley, Benjamin. *A Treatise Concerning the Properties and Effect of Coffee*. London: printed for the author by John Stockdale, 1785.

Morris, Sir Daniel. Suggestions for the Improving the Coffee Industry of Jamaica. Extract from *Productive Industry, A Short Economic History of Jamaica, 1844–1933*.

————. Letter to the editor. *Ceylon Observer*. June 1880.

————. Some Objects of Productive Industry. Lecture delivered at the Town Hall, Kingston. Kingston: MC De Souza, 1884.

Notes on Coffee from Laborie's *Coffee Planter*. Pamphlet. National Library of Jamaica, Kingston.

Pratt, A.M. *Coffee Rehabilitation Scheme*. Pamphlet. Jamaica Ministry of Agriculture and Lands, 1946.

Report to Investigate the Decline of Coffee. Jamaica Ministry of Agriculture and Lands, 1967.

Rodriquez, D.W. *Coffee: A Short Economic History with Special Reference to Jamaica*. Pamphlet. Commodity Bulletin No. 2. Kingston: Government printer for Ministry of Agriculture & Lands, 1961.

Reekie, Jennie. *The Little Coffee Book*. Chatham: Judy Piatkus (Pubs.) Ltd, 1985.

Roden, Claudia. *Coffee*. Australia: Penguin Books, 1977.

Thurber, Francis Beatty. *Coffee: From Plantation to Cup. A Brief History of Coffee Production and Consumption*. 6th ed. New York: American Grocer, 1884. (University of the West Indies Library, Mona, Kingston, Jamaica).

United Kingdom. Parliament. *First Report from the Select Committee on Sugar and Coffee Planting together with the Minutes of Evidence and Appendix*. 1848.

United Kingdom. Parliament. The Sugar Question being a digest of the evidence taken before the Committee on Sugar and Coffee Plantations, which was moved by Lord Bent, inck, MP. 3 February 1843.

Uribe, Andres. *Brown Gold: The Amazing Story of Coffee*. New York: Random House, 1954.

Wakefield, A.J. The Rehabilitation of the Coffee Industry in Jamaica. Kingston: Government Printing Press, 1945.

Williams, Randolph L. A Comparison of Investment Functions, the Determinants of Capital Expenditure in Jamaica. Kingston: Institute of Social and Economic Research (ISER), University of the West Indies, 1973.

————. Jamaica Coffee Supply 1953–1968: An Exploratory Study. Kingston: ISER, University of the West Indies, 1973.

————. The Growth Structure and Performance of the Coffee Industry of Jamaica. Kingston: ISER, University of the West Indies, 1973.

Yolande, Clive. 'Coffee Production in Jamaica'. *Jamaica Journal* Col. 13, no. 1:188–217.

Index

216